Teacher Annotated Edition

GLENCOE
MATHEMATICS

Noteables™
Interactive Study Notebook

with
FOLDABLES™

Mathematics
Applications and Concepts
Course 3

Contributing Author
Dinah Zike

FOLDABLES™

Consultant
Douglas Fisher, PhD
Director of Professional Development
San Diego State University
San Diego, CA

Mc Graw Hill **Glencoe**

New York, New York   Columbus, Ohio   Chicago, Illinois   Peoria, Illinois   Woodland Hills, California

FOLDABLES™ Have students make this Foldable to help them organize and store their chapter Foldables. Begin with one sheet of 11" × 17" paper.

STEP 1 Fold
Fold the paper in half lengthwise. Then unfold.

STEP 2 Fold and Glue
Fold the paper in half widthwise and glue all of the edges.

STEP 3 Glue and Label
Glue the left, right, and bottom edges of the Foldable to the inside back cover of your Noteables notebook.

Foldables | Organizer

Reading and Taking Notes As students read and study each chapter, they should record notes in their chapter Foldable. Then have students store their chapter Foldables inside this Foldable organizer.

Mc Graw Hill **Glencoe**

The McGraw-Hill Companies

Send all inquiries to:
The McGraw-Hill Companies
8787 Orion Place
Columbus, OH 43240-4027

ISBN: 0-07-868431-5   *Mathematics: Applications and Concepts, Course 3 (Teacher Annotated Edition)*
Noteables™: Interactive Study Notebook with Foldables™

1 2 3 4 5 6 7 8 9 10 009 09 08 07 06 05 04

Contents

Contents

Noteables™ with FOLDABLES™
Interactive Study Notebook
All-in-One Teaching and Learning Tool

> The examples can also be found on the **Interactive Chalkboard CD-ROM.**

> The examples correspond to the In-Class Examples in the margin of the **Teacher Wraparound Edition.**

EXAMPLE Use Square Roots to Solve an Eq...

3 ALGEBRA Solve $x^2 = \frac{49}{64}$.

$x^2 = \frac{49}{64}$ — Write the equation.

$\sqrt{x^2} = \sqrt{\frac{49}{64}}$ or ☐ — Take the square root of each side.

$x = $ ☐ or $-\frac{7}{8}$ — Notice that $\frac{7}{8} \cdot \frac{7}{8} = $ ☐ and

$$\left(-\frac{7}{8}\right)\left(-\frac{7}{8}\right) = \text{☐}.$$

The equation has two solutions, ☐ and ☐.

Your Turn Solve $x^2 = \frac{81}{100}$.

FOLDABLES

ORGANIZE IT
On Lesson 3-1 of your Foldable, explain how to find the square root of a number and give an example.

Chapter 3
Algebra: Real Numbers and the Pythagorean Theorem

EXAMPLE Use an Equation to Solve a Problem

4 MUSIC The art work of the square picture in a compact disc case is approximately 14,161 mm² in area. Find the length of each side.

The area...
Let $A = $ ...

> The **Noteables™: Interactive Study Notebook Transparencies** contain transparencies for each lesson.

> The Your Turn Exercises are also found on the **Interactive Chalkboard CD-ROM.**

...side.

The length... side of a compact disc case is about ☐ millimeter...ince d...

HOMEWORK ASSIGNMENT
Page(s): ___
Exercises: ___

Your Turn A p...
approximately 11...
of each side of the...

Chapter 3   Algebra: Real Numbers and the Pythagorean Theorem   Lesson 3-1

Example 4

MUSIC The art work of the square picture in a compact disc case is approximately 14,161 mm² in area. Find the length of each side of the square.

Words	Area	is equal to	the square of the length of a side.
Variabl...	A	=	s^2
Equation	14,161	=	s^2

Noteables™ with FOLDABLES™
Interactive Study Notebook

This note-taking guide is designed to help students succeed in *Mathematics: Applications and Concepts,* Course 3. Each chapter includes:

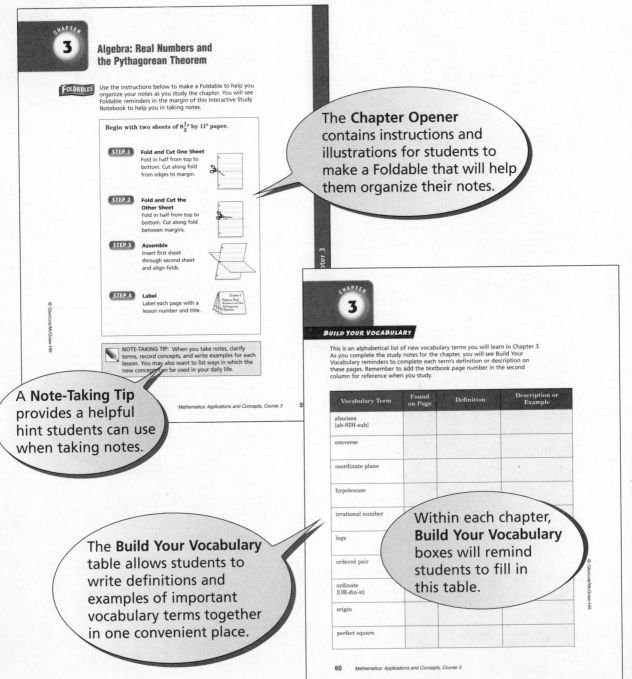

The **Chapter Opener** contains instructions and illustrations for students to make a Foldable that will help them organize their notes.

A **Note-Taking Tip** provides a helpful hint students can use when taking notes.

The **Build Your Vocabulary** table allows students to write definitions and examples of important vocabulary terms together in one convenient place.

Within each chapter, **Build Your Vocabulary** boxes will remind students to fill in this table.

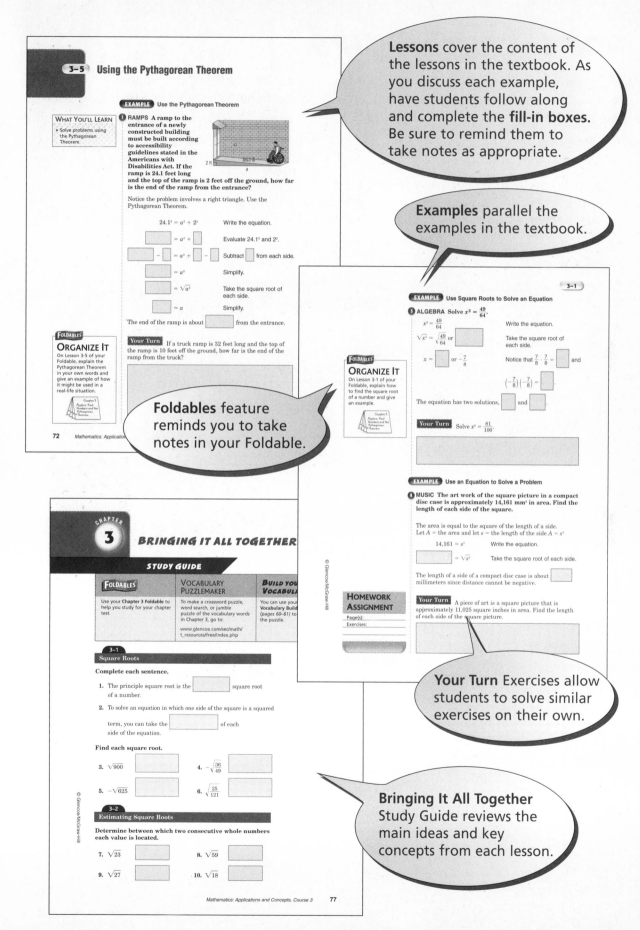

3-5 Using the Pythagorean Theorem

WHAT YOU'LL LEARN
• Solve problems using the Pythagorean Theorem.

EXAMPLE Use the Pythagorean Theorem

① **RAMPS** A ramp to the entrance of a newly constructed building must be built according to accessibility guidelines stated in the Americans with Disabilities Act. If the ramp is 24.1 feet long and the top of the ramp is 2 feet off the ground, how far is the end of the ramp from the entrance?

Notice the problem involves a right triangle. Use the Pythagorean Theorem.

$24.1^2 = a^2 + 2^2$ Write the equation.

$\boxed{} = a^2 + \boxed{}$ Evaluate 24.1^2 and 2^2.

$\boxed{} - \boxed{} = a^2 + \boxed{} - \boxed{}$ Subtract $\boxed{}$ from each side.

$\boxed{} = a^2$ Simplify.

$\boxed{} = \sqrt{a^2}$ Take the square root of each side.

$\boxed{} \approx a$ Simplify.

The end of the ramp is about $\boxed{}$ from the entrance.

FOLDABLES
ORGANIZE IT
On Lesson 3-5 of your Foldable, explain the Pythagorean Theorem in your own words and give an example of how it might be used in a real-life situation.

Your Turn If a truck ramp is 32 feet long and the top of the ramp is 10 feet off the ground, how far is the end of the ramp from the truck?

72   Mathematics: Applications

Lessons cover the content of the lessons in the textbook. As you discuss each example, have students follow along and complete the **fill-in boxes**. Be sure to remind them to take notes as appropriate.

Examples parallel the examples in the textbook.

Foldables feature reminds you to take notes in your Foldable.

3-1

EXAMPLE Use Square Roots to Solve an Equation

③ **ALGEBRA** Solve $x^2 = \frac{49}{64}$.

$x^2 = \frac{49}{64}$ Write the equation.

$\sqrt{x^2} = \sqrt{\frac{49}{64}}$ or $\boxed{}$ Take the square root of each side.

$x = \boxed{}$ or $-\frac{7}{8}$ Notice that $\frac{7}{8} \cdot \frac{7}{8} = \boxed{}$ and

$\left(-\frac{7}{8}\right)\left(-\frac{7}{8}\right) = \boxed{}$

The equation has two solutions, $\boxed{}$ and $\boxed{}$.

FOLDABLES
ORGANIZE IT
On Lesson 3-1 of your Foldable, explain how to find the square root of a number and give an example.

Your Turn Solve $x^2 = \frac{81}{100}$.

EXAMPLE Use an Equation to Solve a Problem

④ **MUSIC** The art work of the square picture in a compact disc case is approximately 14,161 mm² in area. Find the length of each side of the square.

The area is equal to the square of the length of a side.
Let A = the area and let s = the length of the side $A = s^2$

$14,161 = s^2$ Write the equation.

$\boxed{} = \sqrt{s^2}$ Take the square root of each side.

The length of a side of a compact disc case is about $\boxed{}$ millimeters since distance cannot be negative.

HOMEWORK ASSIGNMENT
Page(s):
Exercises:

Your Turn A piece of art is a square picture that is approximately 11,025 square inches in area. Find the length of each side of the square picture.

Your Turn Exercises allow students to solve similar exercises on their own.

CHAPTER 3

BRINGING IT ALL TOGETHER

STUDY GUIDE

FOLDABLES	**VOCABULARY PUZZLEMAKER**	**BUILD YOU VOCABULA**
Use your **Chapter 3 Foldable** to help you study for your chapter test.	To make a crossword puzzle, word search, or jumble puzzle of the vocabulary words in Chapter 3, go to: www.glencoe.com/sec/math/t_resources/free/index.php	You can use your **Vocabulary Build** (pages 60–61) to the puzzle.

3-1
Square Roots

Complete each sentence.

1. The principle square root is the $\boxed{}$ square root of a number.

2. To solve an equation in which one side of the square is a squared term, you can take the $\boxed{}$ of each side of the equation.

Find each square root.

3. $\sqrt{900}$ $\boxed{}$

4. $-\sqrt{\frac{36}{49}}$ $\boxed{}$

5. $-\sqrt{625}$ $\boxed{}$

6. $\sqrt{\frac{25}{121}}$ $\boxed{}$

3-2
Estimating Square Roots

Determine between which two consecutive whole numbers each value is located.

7. $\sqrt{23}$ $\boxed{}$

8. $\sqrt{59}$ $\boxed{}$

9. $\sqrt{27}$ $\boxed{}$

10. $\sqrt{18}$ $\boxed{}$

Mathematics: Applications and Concepts, Course 3   77

Bringing It All Together Study Guide reviews the main ideas and key concepts from each lesson.

NOTE-TAKING TIPS

Notes are a reminder to the students as to what they learned in class. Taking good notes can help students succeed in mathematics. The following tips will help students take better classroom notes.

- Before class, ask what your teacher will be discussing in class. Review mentally what you already know about the concept.

- Be an active listener. Focus on what your teacher is saying. Listen for important concepts. Pay attention to words, examples, and/or diagrams your teacher emphasizes.

- Write your notes as clear and concise as possible. The following symbols and abbreviations may be helpful in your note-taking.

Word or Phrase	Symbol or Abbreviation	Word or Phrase	Symbol or Abbreviation
for example	e.g.	not equal	$\neq$
such as	i.e.	approximately	$\approx$
with	w/	therefore	$\therefore$
without	w/o	versus	vs
and	+	angle	$\angle$

- Use a symbol such as a star (★) or an asterisk (*) to emphasis important concepts. Place a question mark (?) next to anything that you do not understand.

- Ask questions and participate in class discussion.

- Draw and label pictures or diagrams to help clarify a concept.

- When working out an example, write what you are doing to solve the problem next to each step. Be sure to use your own words.

- Review your notes as soon as possible after class. During this time, organize and summarize new concepts and clarify misunderstandings.

Note-Taking Don'ts

- **Don't** write every word. Concentrate on the main ideas and concepts.

- **Don't** use someone else's notes as they may not make sense.

- **Don't** doodle. It distracts you from listening actively.

- **Don't** lose focus or you will become lost in your note-taking.

Algebra: Integers

 Use the instructions below to make a Foldable to help you organize your notes as you study the chapter. You will see Foldable reminders in the margin of this Interactive Study Notebook to help you in taking notes.

Begin with a plain piece of 11" × 17" paper.

STEP 1 **Fold**
Fold the paper in sixths lengthwise.

STEP 2 **Open and Fold**
Fold a 4" tab along the short side. Then fold the rest in half.

STEP 3 **Label**
Draw lines along the folds and label as shown.

	Words	Example(s)
A Plan for Problem Solving		
+ & − of Integers		
× & ÷ of Integers		
Solving + & − Equations		
Solving × & ÷ Equations		

 NOTE-TAKING TIP: When taking notes, it may be helpful to explain each idea in words and give one or more examples.

BUILD YOUR VOCABULARY

This is an alphabetical list of new vocabulary terms you will learn in Chapter 1. As you complete the study notes for the chapter, you will see Build Your Vocabulary reminders to complete each term's definition or description on these pages. Remember to add the textbook page number in the second column for reference when you study.

Vocabulary Term	Found on Page	Definition	Description or Example
absolute value			
additive inverse			
algebraic expression [AL-juh-BRAY-ihk]			
conjecture			
coordinate			
counterexample			
defining a variable			
equation [ih-KWAY-zhuhn]			
evaluate			
inequality			

Vocabulary Term	Found on Page	Definition	Description or Example
integer [IHN-tih-juhr]			
inverse operations			
negative number			
numerical expression			
open sentence			
opposites			
order of operations			
powers			
property			
solution			
solve			
variable			

A Plan for Problem Solving

BUILD YOUR VOCABULARY (pages 2–3)

Some problem solving strategies require you to make an

| educated guess | or **conjecture**.

EXAMPLES Use the Four-Step Plan

FOLDABLES

ORGANIZE IT

Summarize the four-step problem-solving plan in words and symbols. Include an example of how you have used this plan to solve a problem.

	Words	Example(s)
A Plan for Problem Solving		
+ & − of Integers		
× & ÷ of Integers		
Solving + & − Equations		
Solving × & ÷ Equations		

1 HOME IMPROVEMENT The Vorhees family plans to paint the wall in their family room. They need to cover 512 square feet with two coats of paint. If a one-gallon can of paint covers 220 square feet, how many one-gallon cans of paint should they purchase?

EXPLORE Since they will be using **two** coats of paint, we

must **double** the area to be painted.

PLAN They will be covering **512** × **2** square feet

or **1,024** square feet. Next, divide **1,024** by

220 to determine how many cans of paint are needed.

SOLVE **1,024** ÷ **220** = **4.7 cans**

EXAMINE Since they will purchase a whole number of cans of

paint, round **4.7** to **5** .

They will need to purchase **5** cans of paint.

Your Turn Jocelyn plans to paint her bedroom. She needs to cover 400 square feet with three coats of paint. If a one-gallon can of paint covers 350 square feet, how many one-gallon cans of paint should she purchase?

4

REMEMBER IT

Always check to make sure your answer is reasonable. You can solve the problem again if you think your answer is not correct.

2 GEOGRAPHY The five largest states in total area, which includes land and water, are shown. Of the five states shown, which one has the smallest area of water?

Largest States in Area		
State	**Land Area (mi²)**	**Total Area (mi²)**
Alaska	570,374	615,230
Texas	261,914	267,277
California	155,973	158,869
Montana	145,556	147,046
New Mexico	121,364	121,598

Source: U.S. Census Bureau

EXPLORE You are given the total area and the land area for five states. You need to find the water area.

PLAN To determine the water area, **subtract** the **land area** from the **total area** for each state.

SOLVE Alaska = 615,230 − 570,374 = **44,856**

Texas = 267,277 − 261,914 = **5,363**

California = 158,869 − 155,973 = **2,896**

Montana = 147,026 − 145,556 = **1,470**

New Mexico = 121,598 − 121,364 = **234**

EXAMINE Compare the water area for each state to determine which state has the least water area.

New Mexico has the least water area with **234** square miles.

Your Turn Refer to Example 2. How many times larger is the land area of Alaska than the land area of Montana?

about 4 times larger

HOMEWORK ASSIGNMENT

Page(s):

Exercises:

Variables, Expressions, and Properties

WHAT YOU'LL LEARN

- Evaluate expressions and identify properties.

BUILD YOUR VOCABULARY (pages 2–3)

A **variable** is a $\boxed{\text{symbol}}$, usually a letter, used to represent a $\boxed{\text{number}}$.

An **algebraic expression** contains a $\boxed{\text{variable}}$, a number, and at least one $\boxed{\text{operation}}$ symbol.

When you substitute a number for the $\boxed{\text{variable}}$, an algebraic expression becomes a **numeric expression**.

To **evaluate** an expression means to find its $\boxed{\text{numeric}}$ value.

To avoid confusion, mfathematicians have agreed on a $\boxed{\text{set of rules}}$ called the **order of operations**.

KEY CONCEPT

Order of Operations

1. Do all operations within grouping symbols first; start with the innermost grouping symbols.

2. Evaluate all powers before other operations.

3. Multiply and divide in order from left to right.

4. Add and subtract in order from left to right.

EXAMPLE Evaluate a Numerical Expression

❶ Evaluate $3 + 9 - 2 \times (8 \div 2)$.

$3 \div 9 - 2 \times (8 \div 2)$

$= 3 + 9 - 2 \times \boxed{4}$ $\boxed{\textbf{Divide}}$ inside parentheses first.

$= 3 + 9 - \boxed{8}$ $\boxed{\textbf{Multiply}}$ next.

$= \boxed{12} - 8$ or $\boxed{4}$ Add and subtract in order from left to right.

Your Turn Evaluate $2 + 6 - 3 \times (6 \div 3)$.

2

BUILD YOUR VOCABULARY (pages 2–3)

Expressions such as 7^2 and 2^3 are called **powers** and represent repeated | **multiplication** |.

EXAMPLES Evaluate Algebraic Expressions

2 Evaluate the expression $3r + 2s - 4$ if $r = 6$ and $s = 3$.

$3r + 2s - 4 = 3\boxed{(6)} + 2\boxed{(3)} - 4 \qquad r = \boxed{6}, \quad \boxed{s} = 3$

$\qquad\qquad = \boxed{18} + \boxed{6} - 4 \qquad$ Multiply.

$\qquad\qquad = \boxed{20} \qquad\qquad\qquad$ Add and subtract in order from left to right.

3 Evaluate the expression $\dfrac{6q}{3r - 3}$ if $q = 5$ and $r = 6$.

The fraction bar is a grouping symbol. Evaluate the expressions in the numerator and denominator separately before dividing.

$$\frac{6q}{3r - 3} = \frac{6\boxed{(5)}}{3\boxed{(6)} - 3} \qquad q = \boxed{5}, \quad \boxed{r} = 6$$

$$= \frac{\boxed{30}}{\boxed{18} - 3} \qquad \text{Multiply.}$$

$$= \frac{\boxed{30}}{15} \text{ or } \boxed{2} \qquad \text{Subtract in the denominator. Then divide.}$$

Your Turn Evaluate each expression.

a. $2r + 4s - 2$ if $r = 5$ and $s = 4$

| 24 |

b. $\dfrac{3s}{q + 4}$ if $q = 2$ and $s = 4$

| 2 |

A mathematical sentence that contains an | equals | sign (=) is called an **equation**.

An equation that contains a | variable | is an **open sentence**.

Properties are | open | sentences that are true or false for any numbers.

A **counterexample** is an example that shows that a conjecture is | false |.

REMEMBER IT

Commutative Property
$a + b = b + a$
$a \cdot b = b \cdot a$

Associative Property
$a + (b + c) = (a + b) + c$
$a \cdot (b \cdot c) = (a \cdot b) \cdot c$

Distributive Property
$a(b + c) = ab + ac$
$a(b - c) = ab - ac$

Identity Property
$a + 0 = a$
$a \cdot 1 = a$

EXAMPLE Identify Properties

④ **Name the property shown by $12 \cdot 1 = 12$.**

Multiplying by 1 does not change the number.

This is the | **Multiplicative Identity** | Property.

Your Turn Name the property shown by $3 \cdot 2 = 2 \cdot 3$.

Commutative Property of Multiplication

EXAMPLE Find a Counterexample

⑤ **State whether the following conjecture is *true* or *false*.**

The sum of an odd number and an even number is always odd.

This conjecture is | **true** |.

Your Turn State whether the following conjecture is *true* or *false*. If false, provide a counterexample.

Division of whole numbers is associative.

false; $15 \div (6 \div 2) \neq (15 \div 6) \div 2$

HOMEWORK ASSIGNMENT

Page(s):
Exercises:

Integers and Absolute Values

WHAT YOU'LL LEARN

- Graph integers on a number line and find absolute value.

BUILD YOUR VOCABULARY (pages 2–3)

A **negative number** is a number $\boxed{\text{less}}$ than zero.

$\boxed{\text{Negative}}$ numbers, positive numbers and $\boxed{\text{zero}}$ are members of the set of **integers**.

EXAMPLES Write Integers for Real-Life Situations

1 Write an integer to represent a 35¢ discount.

The integer is $\boxed{-35}$.

2 Write an integer for the expression *a fever of 4 degrees above normal.*

The integer is $\boxed{+4}$.

Your Turn Write an integer for each situation.

a. a 25¢ tax $\boxed{+25}$

b. a loss of 10 yards in football $\boxed{-10}$

BUILD YOUR VOCABULARY (pages 2–3)

The $\boxed{\textbf{number}}$ that corresponds to a $\boxed{\textbf{point}}$ is called the **coordinate** of that point.

A sentence that $\boxed{\textbf{compares}}$ two different numbers of quantities is called an **inequality**.

EXAMPLES Compare Two Integers

3 Replace ● in −3 ● 3 with <, >, or = to make a true sentence.

-4 -3 -2 -1 0 1 2 3 4

The number line shows that −3 is ┃ **less** ┃ than 3, since it lies to the ┃ **left** ┃ of 3. So, write −3 ┃ **<** ┃ 3.

Your Turn Replace ● with <, >, or = to make a true sentence.

a. −2 ● 2

┃ **−2 < 2** ┃

b. −4 ● −6

┃ **−4 > −6** ┃

EXAMPLE Order Integers **(parallels Example 5 in text)**

4 FOOTBALL Order the statistics in the table from least to greatest.

Player	Yards Rushing
Marty	8
Autry	4
Shane	5
Brad	−10
Glyn	3
Jim	−19

Graph each integer on a number line.

-20 -18 -16 -14 -12 -10 -8 -6 -4 -2 0 2 4 6 8

The order from least to greatest is ┃ **−19, −10, 3, 4, 5, 8** ┃.

Your Turn Order the temperatures 83°, 81°, −54°, −30° from least to greatest.

┃ **−54°, −30°, 81°, 83°** ┃

BUILD YOUR VOCABULARY (pages 2–3)

The **absolute value** of a number is the distance the number is from $\boxed{0}$ on the number line.

REMEMBER IT

The absolute value of a number is *not* the same as the opposite of a number. Remember that the absolute value of a number cannot be negative.

EXAMPLES Expressions with Absolute Value

Evaluate each expression. **(parallels Example 6 in text)**

5 $|5|$

The graph of 5 is $\boxed{5}$ units from 0 on the number line.

So, $|5| = \boxed{5}$.

6 $|6| - |-5|$ **(parallels Example 7 in text)**

$|6| - |-5| = \boxed{6} - |-5|$ The absolute value of 6 is $\boxed{6}$.

$= 6 - \boxed{5}$ $|-5| = \boxed{5}$

$= \boxed{1}$ Simplify.

7 Evaluate $|x| + 13$ if $x = -4$. **(parallels Example 8 in text)**

$|x| + 13 = |\boxed{-4}| + 13$ Replace x with $\boxed{-4}$.

$= \boxed{4} + 13$ $|-4| = \boxed{4}$

$= \boxed{17}$ Simplify.

Your Turn

Evaluate each expression.

a. $|-3|$

$\boxed{3}$

b. $|9| - |-6|$

$\boxed{3}$

c. Evaluate $|x| \div 7$ if $x = -2$.

$\boxed{9}$

HOMEWORK ASSIGNMENT

Page(s):

Exercises:

Adding Integers

EXAMPLES Add Integers with the Same Sign

1 Find −8 + (−4).

METHOD 1 Use a number line.

Start at zero.

Move ⎡ **8** ⎤ units to the left.

From there, move 4 units ⎡ **left** ⎤.

METHOD 2 Use counters.

−8 + (−4)   −8 + (−4) = −12

So, −8 + (−4) = ⎡ **−12** ⎤.

KEY CONCEPT

Adding Integers with the Same Sign To add integers with the same sign, add their absolute values. Give the result the same sign as the integers.

2 Find −21 + (−5).

−21 + (−5) = ⎡ **−26** ⎤

Add |−21| and |−5|. Both numbers are negative, so the sum is negative.

Your Turn Add using a number line or counters.

a. −3 + (−6)

−9

b. −13 + (−12)

−25

EXAMPLES Add Integers with Different Signs

3 **Find 4 + (−6).**

You can use a number line or counters to find the sum. Use a number line.

Start at [**zero**].

Move 4 units [**right**].

From there, move [**6**] units left.

So, 4 + (−6) = [**−2**].

4 **Find −5 + 9.**

Use Counters to find the sum.

−5 + 9   =   −5 + 9 = 4

So, −5 + 9 = [**4**].

EXAMPLE Add Integers with Different Signs

5 **Find 33 + (−16).**

33 + (−16) = [**17**]

To find 33 + (−16), subtract |−16| from |33|.

The sum is [**positive**]

because |33| > |−16|.

FOLDABLES

ORGANIZE IT

Explain and give examples of how to add integers with the same sign and how to add integers with a different signs.

	Words	Example(s)
A Plan for Problem Solving		
+ & − of Integers		
× & ÷ of Integers		
Solving + & − Equations		
Solving × & ÷ Equations		

KEY CONCEPT

Adding Integers with Different Signs To add integers with different signs, subtract their absolute values. Give the result the same sign as the integer with the greater absolute value.

Your Turn

Add.

a. $3 + (-5)$

-2

b. $-6 + 8$

2

c. $25 + (-15)$.

10

BUILD YOUR VOCABULARY (pages 2–3)

Two numbers with the same **absolute value** but different signs are called **opposites**.

An integer and its **opposite** are also called **additive inverses**.

EXAMPLES   Add Three or More Integers

6 **Find each sum.**

$2 + (-5) + (-3)$

$2 + (-5) + (-3) = 2 + [\boxed{-5} + (-3)]$ Associative Property

$= 2 + \boxed{(-8)}$ Order of operations.

$= \boxed{-6}$ Simplify.

KEY CONCEPT

Additive Inverse Property The sum of any number and its additive inverse is zero.

7 $-17 + 6 + 17 + 20$

$-7 + 6 + 17 + 20$

$= -17 + 17 + \boxed{6} + 20$ Commutative Property

$= (-17 + 17) + (6 + 20)$ Associative Property

$= \boxed{0} + \boxed{26}$ Additive Inverse Property

$= \boxed{26}$ Simplify.

Your Turn Find each sum.

a. $3 + (-6) + (-2)$

-9

b. $-10 + 5 + 10 + 7$

-25

8 **STOCKS** An investor owns 50 shares in a video game manufacturer. A broker purchases 30 shares more for the client on Tuesday. On Friday, the investor asks the broker to sell 65 shares. How many shares of this stock will the client own after these trades are completed?

Selling a stock decreases the number of shares, so the integer for selling is -65 .

Purchasing new stock increases the number of shares, so the integer for buying is $+30$.

Add these integers to the starting number of shares to find the new number of shares.

$50 +$ 30 $+ ($ -65 $)$

$= (50 +$ 30 $) + ($ -65 $)$ Associative Property

$=$ 80 $+ (-65)$ $50 +$ 30 $=$ 80

$=$ 15 Simplify.

Your Turn Jaime gets an allowance of $5. She spends $2 on video games and $1 on lunch. Her best friend repays a $2 loan and she buys a $3 pair of socks. How much money does Jaime have left?

$1

HOMEWORK ASSIGNMENT

Page(s):

Exercises:

1-5 Subtracting Integers

EXAMPLES Subtract a Positive Integer

WHAT YOU'LL LEARN

• Subtract integers.

1 Find 2 − 6.

$$2 - 6 = 2 + (-6)$$ To subtract 6, add $\boxed{-6}$.

$$= \boxed{-4}$$ Add.

2 Find −7 − 5.

$$-7 - 5 = -7 \boxed{+} (-5)$$ To subtract $\boxed{5}$ add −5.

$$= -12$$ Add.

KEY CONCEPT

Subtracting Integers

To subtract an integer, add its opposite or additive inverse.

EXAMPLES Subtract a Negative Integer

3 Find 11 − (−8).

$$11 - (-8) = \boxed{11} - 8$$ To subtract −8, add $\boxed{8}$.

$$= \boxed{19}$$ Add.

4 Find −6 − (−9).

$$-6 - (-9) = -6 \boxed{+9}$$ To subtract $\boxed{-8}$, add $\boxed{9}$.

$$= \boxed{3}$$ Add.

FOLDABLES

ORGANIZE IT

Record in your Foldable how to subtract integers. Be sure to include examples.

	Words	Example(s)
A Plan for Problem Solving		
+ & − of Integers		
× & ÷ of Integers		
Solving + & − Equations		
Solving × & ÷ Equations		

Your Turn Subtract.

a. 3 − 7

$$\boxed{-4}$$

b. −6 − 2

$$\boxed{-8}$$

c. 15 − (−3)

$$\boxed{19}$$

d. −7 − (−11)

$$\boxed{-4}$$

WRITE IT

Explain why −b does not necessarily mean that the value of −b is negative.

_____

_____

_____

_____

EXAMPLES Evaluate Algebraic Expressions

5 Evaluate $12 − r$ if $r = −7$.

$12 − r = 12 −$ | (−7)   Replace r with | −7 .

    $= 12 +$ | 7   To subtract | −7 add | 7 .

    $=$ | 19   Add.

6 Evaluate $q − p$ if $p = 6$ and $q = −3$.

$q − p = −3 − 6$ Replace q with | −3 and

                     p with | 6 .

    $= −3 +$ | (−6)   To subtract | 6 , add | (−6) .

    $=$ | −9   Add.

Your Turn Evaluate each expression if $a = 3$, $b = −6$, and $c = 2$.

a. $10 − c$ **b.** $b − a$

−9   −9

HOMEWORK ASSIGNMENT

Page(s): _____

Exercises: _____

_____

_____

Multiplying and Dividing Integers

WHAT YOU'LL LEARN

- Multiply and divide integers.

KEY CONCEPTS

Multiplying Two Integers
The product of two integers with different signs is negative.

The product of two integers with the same sign is positive.

Dividing Integers The quotient of two integers with different signs is negative.

The quotient of two integers with the same sign is positive.

REMEMBER IT

Decide on the sign of the product before multiplying. If the number of negatives is *even* the product is positive. If the number of negatives is *odd* the product is negative.

EXAMPLE Multiply Integers with Different Signs

1 Find $8(-4)$.

$$8(-4) = \boxed{-32}$$

The factors have $\boxed{\text{different}}$ signs. The product is $\boxed{\text{negative}}$.

EXAMPLE Multiply Integers with the Same Sign

2 Find $-12(-12)$. **(parallels Example 3 in text)**

$$-12(-12) = \boxed{144}$$

The factors have the $\boxed{\text{same}}$ sign. The product is $\boxed{\text{positive}}$.

EXAMPLE Multiply More Than Two Integers

3 Find $6(-2)(-4)$. **(parallels Example 4 in text)**

$$6(-2)(-4) = [6(-2)] \boxed{(-4)} \quad \boxed{\text{Associative}} \text{ Property}$$

$$= -12 \boxed{(-4)} \qquad 6(-2) = \boxed{-12}$$

$$= \boxed{48} \qquad -12(-4) = \boxed{48}$$

Your Turn Multiply.

a. $6(-3)$

$$\boxed{-18}$$

b. $-2(6)$

$$\boxed{-12}$$

c. $-8(-8)$

$$\boxed{64}$$

d. $5(-3)(-2)$

$$\boxed{30}$$

EXAMPLES Divide Integers

4 Find 30 ÷ −5. **(parallels Example 5 in text)**

$30 \div -5 =$ **−6**

The dividend and the divisor have **different** signs.

The quotient is **negative** .

FOLDABLES

ORGANIZE IT

Describe why the product or quotient of two integers with the same sign is positive and the product or quotient of two integers with different signs is negative.

	Words	Example(s)
A Plan for Problem Solving		
+ & − of Integers		
× & ÷ of Integers		
Solving + & − Equations		
Solving × & ÷ Equations		

Your Turn Divide.

a. 36 ÷ (−6).

−6

b. $\frac{-30}{5}$

−6

EXAMPLE Evaluate Algebraic Expressions

5 Evaluate −3x − (−4y) if x = −10 and y = −4.

3x − (−4y)   **(parallels Example 5 in text)**

= 3(**−10**) − [−4(**−4**)]   Replace x with **−10** and y with **−4** .

= **−30** − **16**   3(−10) = **−30**

   −4(−4) = **16**

= −30 + **(−16)**   To subtract **16** , add **−16** .

= **−46**   Add.

Your Turn Evaluate 2a − (−3b) if a = 26 and b = 24.

−24

EXAMPLE Find the Mean of a Set of Integers

6 WEATHER The table shows the low temperature for each month in McGrath, Alaska. Find the mean (average) of all 12 temperatures.

To find the mean of a set of numbers, find the sum of the numbers. Then divide the result by how many numbers there are in the set.

Average Low Temperatures	
Month	Temp. (°C)
Jan.	−27
Feb.	−26
March	−19
April	−9
May	1
June	7
July	9
Aug.	7
Sept.	2
Oct.	−8
Nov.	−19
Dec.	−26

Source: weather.com

$$\frac{-27 + (-26) + (-19) + (-9) + 1 + 7 + 9 + 7 + 2 + (-8) + (-19) + (-26)}{12}$$

$$= \frac{\boxed{-108}}{12}$$

$$= \boxed{-9}$$

Your Turn The table shows a set of record low temperatures. Find the mean (average) of all 12 temperatures.

about 12.2°F

Record Low Temperatures	
Month	Temp. (°C)
Jan.	−20
Feb.	−15
March	−5
April	10
May	25
June	31
July	41
Aug.	38
Sept.	34
Oct.	19
Nov.	3
Dec.	−15

Source: weather.com

HOMEWORK ASSIGNMENT

Page(s):

Exercises:

Writing Expressions and Equations

WHAT YOU'LL LEARN

- Write algebraic expressions and equations from verbal phrases and sentences.

BUILD YOUR VOCABULARY (pages 2–3)

When you choose a variable and an unknown quantity for the variable to represent, this is called **defining the variable**.

EXAMPLES Write an Algebraic Expression

1 Write *double the price of a loaf of bread* as an algebraic expression.

Words	double the price of a loaf of bread
Variable	Let *p* represent the price of a **loaf of bread**.
Expression	double the price of a loaf of bread

$$2 \cdot p$$

The expression is **2p**.

2 Write *stalks of celery are divided into 4 portions* as an algebraic expression.

Words	Stalks of celery are divided into 4 portions.
Variable	Let *c* represent the **stalks of celery**.
Expression	Stalks of celery are divided into 4 portions

$$c \quad \div \quad 4$$

The expression is $\dfrac{c}{4}$.

REMEMBER IT

It is often helpful to select letters that can easily be connected to the quantity they represent. For example, age = *a*.

Your Turn Write each verbal sentence as an algebraic expression.

a. triple the cost of a cup of coffee $3c$

b. pies are divided into 8 portions $\dfrac{p}{8}$

REVIEW IT

Explain why it is important to read a word problem more than once before attempting to solve it.

_____

_____

_____

_____

_____

EXAMPLE Write an Algebraic Equation

3 Write *the price of a book plus $5 shipping is $29* as an algebraic equation.

Words	The price of a book plus $5 shipping is $29.
▼	
Variable	Let p represent the price of the book.
▼	
Equation	

The price of a book	plus	$5 shipping	is $29.
p	$+$	5	$= 29$

The equation is $p + 5 = 29$.

Your Turn Write *the price of a toy plus $6 shipping is $35* as an algebraic equation.

$p + 6 = 35$

EXAMPLE Write an Equation to Solve a Problem

4 NUTRITION A particular box of oatmeal contains 10 individual packages. If the box contains 30 grams of fiber, write an equation to find the amount of fiber in one package of oatmeal.

Words	Ten packages of oatmeal contain 30 grams of fiber.
▼	
Variable	Let f represent the grams of fiber per package.
▼	
Equation	

Ten packages of oatmeal	contain	30 grams of fiber.
$10f$	$=$	30

© Glencoe/McGraw-Hill

HOMEWORK ASSIGNMENT

Page(s): _____

Exercises: _____

Your Turn A particular box of cookies contains 10 servings. If the box contains 1,200 calories, write an equation to find the number of calories in one serving of cookies.

$10c = 1{,}200$

Solving Addition and Subtraction Equations

WHAT YOU'LL LEARN

- Solve equations using the Subtraction and Addition Properties of Equality.

KEY CONCEPTS

Subtraction Property of Equality If you subtract the same number from each side of an equation, the two sides remain equal.

Addition Property of Equality If you add the same number to each side of an equation, the two sides remain equal.

BUILD YOUR VOCABULARY (pages 2–3)

When you **solve** an equation, you are trying to find the values of the variable that makes the equation | **true** |.

A **solution** is the value of the variable that makes the variable | **true** |.

EXAMPLE Solve an Addition Equation

1 Solve $7 = 15 + c$.

METHOD 1 Vertical Method

$$7 = 15 + c$$ Write the equation.

$$7 = 15 + c$$
$$-15 = -15$$ Subtract | 15 | from each side.

| **−8** | $= \quad c$ $7 - 15 =$ | **−8** |; $15 - 15 =$ | **0** |

METHOD 2 Horizontal Method

$$7 = 15 + c$$ Write the equation.

$7 -$ | **15** | $= 15 + c -$ | **15** | Subtract | **15** | from each side.

| **−8** | $= c$ $7 - 15 =$ | **−8** |; and

| **15** | $- 15 = 0$

Your Turn Solve $6 = 11 + a$.

−5

Addition and subtraction are called **inverse operations** because they "undo" each other.

ORGANIZE IT

Compare how to solve an equation involving whole numbers and an equation involving integers.

	Words	Example(s)
A Plan for Problem Solving		
+ & − of Integers		
× & ÷ of Integers		
Solving + & − Equations		
Solving × & ÷ Equations		

EXAMPLE Solve a Subtraction Equation

2 Solve $z - 16 = -5$.

Use the horizontal method.

$z - 16 = 5$ — Write the equation.

$z - 16 + \boxed{16} = -5 + \boxed{16}$ — Add $\boxed{16}$ to each side.

$z = \boxed{11}$ — $-16 + 16 = \boxed{0}$ and

$\boxed{-5} + 16 = 11.$

Your Turn Solve $x - 12 = 26$.

6

EXAMPLE Write and Solve an Equation

3 What value of y makes the difference of 30 and y equal to 12?

$30 - y = 12$ — Write the equation.

$30 - y + y = 12 + y$ — $\boxed{\text{Add}}$ y to each side.

$\boxed{30} = 12 + y$ — $\boxed{-y} + y = 0$

$30 - 12 = 12 - 12 + y$ — $\boxed{\text{Subtract}}$ 12 from each side.

$18 = \boxed{y}$ — $30 - 12 = \boxed{18}$

Your Turn What value of x makes the difference of 30 and x equal to 5?

25

HOMEWORK ASSIGNMENT

Page(s):

Exercises:

Solving Multiplication and Division Equations

WHAT YOU'LL LEARN

• Solve equations by using the Division and Multiplication Properties of Equality.

KEY CONCEPTS

Division Property of Equality If you divide each side of an equation by the same nonzero number, the two sides remain equal.

Multiplication Property of Equality If you multiply each side of an equation by the same number, the two sides remain equal.

EXAMPLE Solve a Multiplication Equation

1 Solve $7z = -49$.

$7z = -49$ Write the equation.

$$\frac{7z}{\boxed{7}} = \frac{-49}{\boxed{7}}$$ $\boxed{\textbf{Divide}}$ each side by $\boxed{7}$.

$\boxed{1}\,z = \boxed{-7}$ $7 \div 7 = \boxed{1}$, $-49 \div 7 = \boxed{-7}$

$\boxed{z} = \boxed{-7}$ Identity Property; $1z = \boxed{z}$

EXAMPLE Solve a Division Equation

2 Solve $\frac{c}{9} = 26$.

$\frac{c}{9} = -6$ Write the equation.

$\frac{c}{9}\,\boxed{(9)} = -6\,\boxed{(9)}$ Multiply each since by $\boxed{9}$.

$c = \boxed{-54}$ $-6\,\boxed{(9)} = \boxed{-54}$

EXAMPLE Use an Equation to Solve a Problem

3 SURVEYING English mathematician Edmund Gunter lived around 1600. He invented the *chain*, which was used to measure land for maps and deeds. One chain equals 66 feet. If the south side of a property measures 330 feet, how many chains long is it?

Words	One chain equals 66 feet.
▼ Variable	Let c = the number of chains in $\boxed{330}$ feet.
▼ Equation	Measurement of property is 66 times the number of chains.

$$330 = \boxed{66c}$$

ORGANIZE IT

On your Foldable table, explain how to solve multiplication equations using the multiplication properties of equality.

	Words	Example(s)
A Plan for Problem Solving		
+ & − of Integers		
× & ÷ of Integers		
Solving + & − Equations		
Solving × & ÷ Equations		

Solve the equation.

$$330 = 66c$$ Write the equation.

$$\frac{330}{\boxed{66}} = \frac{66c}{\boxed{66}}$$ Divide each side by $\boxed{66}$.

$$\boxed{5} = \boxed{c}$$ $330 \div \boxed{66} = \boxed{5}$

The number of chains in 330 feet is $\boxed{5}$.

Your Turn

a. Solve $8a = -64$.

$$\boxed{-8}$$

b. Solve $\frac{x}{5} = -10$.

$$\boxed{-50}$$

c. Most horses are measured in *hands*. One hand equals 4 inches. If a horse measures 60 inches, how many hands is it?

$$\boxed{15 \text{ hands}}$$

HOMEWORK ASSIGNMENT

Page(s):

Exercises:

BRINGING IT ALL TOGETHER

STUDY GUIDE

FOLDABLES™	**VOCABULARY PUZZLEMAKER**	**BUILD YOUR VOCABULARY**
Use your **Chapter 1 Foldable** to help you study for your chapter test.	To make a crossword puzzle, word search, or jumble puzzle of the vocabulary words in Chapter 1, go to: www.glencoe.com/sec/math/t_resources/free/index.php	You can use your completed **Vocabulary Builder** (pages 2-3) to help you solve the puzzle.

1-1
A Plan for Problem Solving

Use the four step plan to solve the problem.

1. Lisa plans to redecorate her bedroom. Each wall is 120 square feet. Three walls need a single coat of paint and the fourth wall needs a double coat. If each can of paint will cover 200 square feet, how many gallons of paint does Lisa need?

> **4 cans**

1-2
Variables, Expressions and Properties

2. Number the operations in the correct order for simplifying $2 + 4(9 - 6 \div 3)$.

4 addition	**2** subtraction
3 multiplication	**1** division

3. Describe how the expressions $2 + 5$ and $5 + 2$ are different. Then determine whether the two expressions are equal to each other. If the expressions are equal, name the property that says they are equal.

> **The numbers are being added in opposite orders; equal; Commutative Property of Addition.**

1-3

Integers and Absolute Values

Complete each sentence with either *left* or *right* to make a true sentence. Then write a statement comparing the two numbers with either < or >.

4. −45 lies to the | left | of 0 on a number line. | −45 < 0 |

5. 72 lies to the | right | of 0 on a number line. | 72 > 0 |

6. −3 lies to the | right | of −95 on a number line. | −3 > −95 |

7. 6 lies to the | right | of −7 on a number line. | 6 > −7 |

1-4

Adding Integers

Determine whether you *add* or *subtract* the absolute values of the numbers to find the sum. Give reasons for your answers.

8. 4 + 8 | **add; same signs** |

9. −3 + 5 | **subtract; different signs** |

10. 9 + (−12) | **subtract; different signs** |

11. −23 + (−16) | **add; same signs** |

1-5

Subtracting Integers

Rewrite each difference as a sum. Then find the sum.

12. 2 − 9 | **2 + (−9); −7** |

13. −3 − 8 | **−3 + −8; −11** |

14. 10 − (−12) | **10 + 12; 22** |

15. −5 − (−16) | **−5 + 16; 11** |

1-6

Multiplying and Dividing Integers

Find each product or quotient.

16. $9(-2)$ `−18`　　**17.** $-6(-7)$ `42`

18. $12 \div (-4)$ `−3`　　**19.** $-35 \div (-7)$ `5`

1-7

Writing Expressions and Equations

Determine whether each situation requires *addition, subtraction, multiplication* **or** *division.*

20. Find the difference in the cost of a gallon of premium gasoline and the cost of a gallon of regular gasoline. **subtraction**

21. Find the flight time after the time has been increased by 15 minutes.

addition

1-8

Solving Addition and Subtraction Equations

Solve each equation.

22. $x + 6 = 9$ `3`　　**23.** $s - 5 = 14$ `19`

24. $4 = -3 + p$ `7`　　**25.** $11 + m = 33$ `22`

1-9

Solving Multiplication and Division Equations

Solve each equation.

26. $8r = 32$ `4`　　**27.** $3 = \frac{x}{7}$ `21`　　**28.** $-9 = -9g$ `1`

ARE YOU READY FOR THE CHAPTER TEST?

Math Online

Visit **msmath3.net** to access your textbook, more examples, self-check quizzes, and practice tests to help you study the concepts in Chapter 1.

Check the one that applies. Suggestions to help you study are given with each item.

☐ **I completed the review of all or most lessons without using my notes or asking for help.**

• You are probably ready for the Chapter Test.

• You may want take the Chapter 1 Practice Test on page 57 of your textbook as a final check.

☐ **I used my Foldable or Study Notebook to complete the review of all or most lessons.**

• You should complete the Chapter 1 Study Guide and Review on pages 54–56 of your textbook.

• If you are unsure of any concepts or skills, refer back to the specific lesson(s).

• You may also want to take the Chapter 1 Practice Test on page 57 of your textbook.

☐ **I asked for help from someone else to complete the review of all or most lessons.**

• You should review the examples and concepts in your Study Notebook and Chapter 1 Foldable.

• Then complete the Chapter 1 Study Guide and Review on pages 54–56 of your textbook.

• If you are unsure of any concepts or skills, refer back to the specific lesson(s).

• You may also want to take the Chapter 1 Practice Test on page 57 of your textbook.

Student Signature   Parent/Guardian Signature

Teacher Signature

Algebra: Rational Numbers

 Use the instructions below to make a Foldable to help you organize your notes as you study the chapter. You will see Foldable reminders in the margin of this Interactive Study Notebook to help you in taking notes.

Begin with $8\frac{1}{2}'' \times 11''$ **paper.**

STEP 1 **Stack pages**
Place 5 sheets of paper $\frac{3}{4}$ inch apart.

STEP 2 **Roll Up Bottom Edges**
All tabs should be the same size.

STEP 3 **Crease and Staple**
Staple along the fold.

STEP 4 **Label**
Label the tabs with the lesson numbers.

Algebra:
Rational Numbers
2-1
2-2
2-3
2-4
2-5
2-6
2-7
2-8
2-9

 NOTE-TAKING TIP: As you study a lesson, write down questions you have, comments and reactions, short summaries of the lesson, and key points that are highlighted and underlined.

Chapter 2

BUILD YOUR VOCABULARY

This is an alphabetical list of new vocabulary terms you will learn in Chapter 2.
As you complete the study notes for the chapter, you will see Build Your
Vocabulary reminders to complete each term's definition or description on
these pages. Remember to add the textbook page number in the second
column for reference when you study.

Vocabulary Term	Found on Page	Definition	Description or Example
bar notation			
base			
dimensional analysis			
exponent			
like fractions			
multiplicative inverses			

Vocabulary Term	Found on Page	Definition	Description or Example
power			
rational number			
reciprocals			
repeating decimal			
scientific notation			
terminating decimal			
unlike fractions			

Fractions and Decimals

WHAT YOU'LL LEARN

• Express rational numbers as decimals and decimals as fractions.

A **rational number** is any number that can be expressed in the form $\frac{a}{b}$ where a and b are $\boxed{\textbf{integers}}$ and $b \neq 0$.

A decimal like 0.0625 is a **terminating** decimal because the division ends, or terminates, when the $\boxed{\textbf{remainder}}$ is 0.

KEY CONCEPT

Rational Numbers A rational number is any number that can be expressed in the form a/b, where a and b are integers and $b \neq 0$.

EXAMPLE Write a Fraction as a Decimal

① Write $\frac{3}{16}$ as a decimal.

$\frac{3}{16}$ means $3 \boxed{\div} 16$.

$$
\begin{array}{r}
0.1875 \\
16\overline{)3.0000} \\
\underline{16} \\
140 \\
\underline{128} \\
120 \\
\underline{112} \\
80 \\
\underline{80} \\
0
\end{array}
$$

Add a decimal point and zeroes to the dividend: $3 = 3.0000$

Division ends when the $\boxed{\textbf{remainder}}$ is 0.

You can also use a calculator.

The fraction $\frac{3}{16}$ can be written as $\boxed{\textbf{0.1875}}$.

Your Turn Write $\frac{1}{16}$ as a decimal.

0.0625

BUILD YOUR VOCABULARY (pages 32–33)

A   **decimal**   like 1.6666 . . . is called a **repeating decimal**.

Since it is not possible to show all of the   **digits** , you

can use **bar notation** to show that the 6   **repeats** .

EXAMPLE   Write a Mixed Number as a Decimal

2 Write $3\frac{2}{11}$ as a decimal.

$3\frac{2}{11}$ means $3 +$ $\dfrac{2}{11}$. To change $\frac{2}{11}$ to a decimal,

divide **2** by **11** .

$$
\begin{array}{r}
0.1818\ldots \\
11\overline{)2.0000} \\
\underline{11} \\
90 \\
\underline{88} \\
20 \\
\underline{11} \\
90 \\
\underline{88} \\
2
\end{array}
$$

The three dots means the one and eight keep repeating.

The remainder after each step is 2 or 9.

The mixed number $3\frac{2}{11}$ can be written as

3 + 0.1818 . . . or 3.1818. . . .

Your Turn   Write $5\frac{1}{9}$ as a decimal.

5.1111 . . .

WRITE IT

Explain how you decide where the bar is placed when you use bar notation for a repeating decimal.

_____

_____

_____

_____

_____

_____

FOLDABLES

ORGANIZE IT

Under the tab for Lesson 2–1, explain in your own words how to express rational numbers as decimals and decimals as fractions.

Algebra:
Rational Numbers
2-1
2-2
2-3
2-4
2-5
2-6
2-7
2-8
2-9

Mathematics: Applications and Concepts, Course 3

EXAMPLE Write a Terminating Decimal as a Fraction

3 Write 0.32 as a fraction. **(parallels Example 4 in text)**

$0.32 = \dfrac{32}{\boxed{100}}$ 0.32 is 32 $\boxed{\textbf{hundredths}}$.

$= \dfrac{8}{\boxed{25}}$ Simplify. Divide by the greatest

common factor of 32 and 100, $\boxed{4}$.

The decimal 0.32 can be written as $\boxed{\dfrac{8}{25}}$.

Your Turn Write 0.16 as a fraction.

$\dfrac{4}{25}$

EXAMPLE Write a Repeating Decimal as a Fraction

4 **ALGEBRA** Write $2.\overline{7}$ as a mixed number.
(parallels Example 5 in text)

Let $N = 2.\overline{7}$ or 2.777 . . . . Then $10N = \boxed{\textbf{27.777 . . .}}$.

Multiply N by $\boxed{10}$ because 1 digit repeats.

Subtract $N = 2.777$ . . . to eliminate the $\boxed{\textbf{repeating}}$ part,
0.777 . . . .

$\begin{aligned} 10N &= 27.777 \ldots \\ -1N &= 2.777 \ldots \end{aligned}$ $N = 1N$

$\boxed{9N} = 25$ $10N - 1N = \boxed{9N}$

$\dfrac{\boxed{9N}}{9} = \dfrac{\boxed{25}}{9}$ Divide each side by $\boxed{9}$.

$N = \boxed{2\dfrac{7}{9}}$ Simplify.

Your Turn Write $1.\overline{7}$ as a mixed number.

$1\dfrac{7}{9}$

HOMEWORK ASSIGNMENT

Page(s):

Exercises:

Comparing and Ordering Rational Numbers

WHAT YOU'LL LEARN
- Compare and order rational numbers.

EXAMPLE Compare Rational Numbers

1 Replace ● with <, >, or = to make $\frac{3}{7}$ ● $\frac{8}{13}$ a true sentence.

METHOD 1 Write as fractions with the same denominator.

For $\frac{3}{7}$ and $\frac{8}{13}$, the least common denominator is 91.

$$\frac{3}{7} = \frac{3 \cdot \boxed{13}}{7 \cdot \boxed{13}} = \frac{\boxed{39}}{91}$$

$$\frac{8}{13} = \frac{8 \cdot \boxed{7}}{13 \cdot \boxed{7}} = \frac{\boxed{56}}{91}$$

Since $\dfrac{\boxed{39}}{91} < \dfrac{\boxed{56}}{91}$, $\frac{3}{7}$ $\boxed{<}$ $\frac{8}{13}$.

METHOD 2 Write as decimals.

Write $\frac{3}{7}$ and $\frac{8}{13}$ as decimals. Use a calculator.

3 ÷ 7 [ENTER =] 0.42857 . . .   8 ÷ 13 [ENTER =] 0.61538 . . .

So, $\frac{3}{7}$ = 0.42857 . . . .   So, $\frac{8}{13}$ = 0.61538 . . . .

Since 0.42857 . . . < 0.61538 . . . , $\boxed{\frac{3}{7}}$ < $\boxed{\frac{8}{13}}$.

FOLDABLES

ORGANIZE IT
Under the tab for Lesson 2–2, explain how you can compare two numbers by expressing them as decimals and comparing the decimals.

Algebra:
Rational Numbers
2-1
2-2
2-3
2-4
2-5
2-6
2-7
2-8
2-9

EXAMPLE Compare Negative Rational Numbers

2 Replace ● with <, >, or = to make -6.7 ● $-6\frac{3}{4}$ a true sentence.

Write $-6\frac{3}{4}$ as a decimal.

$\frac{3}{4}$ = $\boxed{0.75}$, so $-6\frac{3}{4}$ = $\boxed{-6.75}$.

Since $-6.7 > -6.75$, -6.7 $\boxed{>}$ $-6\frac{3}{4}$.

Your Turn Replace each ● with <, >, or = to make a true sentence.

a. $\frac{2}{3}$ ● $\frac{3}{5}$

$$\frac{2}{3} > \frac{3}{5}$$

b. -2.1 ● $-2\frac{1}{8}$

$$-2.1 > -2\frac{1}{8}$$

EXAMPLE Order Rational Numbers

3 CHEMISTRY The values for the approximate densities of various substances are shown in the table. Order the densities from least to greatest.

Write each fraction as a decimal.

$1\frac{4}{5} = $ **1.8**

$2\frac{1}{4} = $ **2.25**

$2\frac{3}{5} = $ **2.6**

Substance	Density (g/cm3)
aluminum	2.7
beryllium	1.87
brick	$1\frac{4}{5}$
crown glass	$2\frac{1}{4}$
fused silica	$2.\overline{2}$
marble	$2\frac{3}{5}$
nylon	1.1
pyrex glass	2.32
rubber neoprene	$1.\overline{3}$

Source: *CRC Handbook of Chemistry and Physics*

From the least to the greatest, the densities are 1.1, $1.\overline{3}$, $1\frac{4}{5}$, 1.87, $2.\overline{2}$, $2\frac{1}{4}$, 2.32, $2\frac{3}{5}$, and 2.7. So, the nylon is the least dense, and aluminum is the most dense.

Your Turn The ride times for five amusement park attractions are shown in the table. Order the lengths from least to greatest.

$$1.5, 1\frac{3}{4}, 1.8,$$
$$2\frac{1}{12}, 2.\overline{3}$$

Coaster	Ride Time (min)
Big Dipper	$1\frac{3}{4}$
Double Loop	1.5
Mind Eraser	1.8
Serial Thriller	$2\frac{1}{12}$
X–Flight	$2.\overline{3}$

Source: www.coasterglobe.com

Multiplying Rational Numbers

WHAT YOU'LL LEARN
• Multiply fractions.

BUILD YOUR VOCABULARY (pages 32–33)

Dimensional analysis is the process of including units of

| measurement | when you | compute | .

EXAMPLE Multiply Fractions

1 Find $\dfrac{3}{7} \cdot \dfrac{8}{9}$. Write in simplest form.

KEY CONCEPT

Multiply Fractions To multiply fractions, multiply the numerators and multiply the denominators.

$$\frac{3}{7} \cdot \frac{8}{9} = \frac{\overset{1}{\cancel{3}}}{7} \cdot \frac{8}{\underset{3}{\cancel{9}}}$$

Divide 3 and 9 by their GCF, **3** .

$$= \frac{\boxed{1 \cdot 8}}{\boxed{7 \cdot 3}}$$

⟵ Multiply the numerators.

⟵ Multiply the denominators.

$$= \frac{8}{21}$$

Simplify.

EXAMPLE Multiply Negative Fractions

2 Find $-\dfrac{3}{4} \cdot \dfrac{7}{12}$. Write in simplest form.

$$-\frac{3}{4} \cdot \frac{7}{12} = -\frac{\overset{-1}{\cancel{3}}}{4} \cdot \frac{7}{\underset{4}{\cancel{12}}}$$

Divide −3 and 12 by their GCF, **3** .

$$= \frac{\boxed{-1 \cdot 7}}{\boxed{4 \cdot 4}}$$

⟵ Multiply the numerators.

⟵ Multiply the denominators.

$$= -\frac{\boxed{7}}{\boxed{16}}$$

The factors have different signs, so the product is negative.

FOLDABLES™

ORGANIZE IT

Under the tab for Lesson 2–3, explain in your own words how to multiply rational numbers.

EXAMPLE Multiply Mixed Numbers

3 Find $3\frac{1}{5} \cdot 1\frac{3}{4}$. Write in simplest form.

$$3\frac{1}{5} \cdot 1\frac{3}{4} = \boxed{\frac{16}{5}} \cdot \boxed{\frac{7}{4}} \qquad 3\frac{1}{5} = \boxed{\frac{16}{5}}, \ 1\frac{3}{4} = \boxed{\frac{7}{4}}$$

$$= \frac{\overset{4}{\cancel{16}}}{5} \cdot \frac{7}{\underset{1}{\cancel{4}}} \qquad \text{Divide 16 and 4 by their GCF, } \boxed{4}.$$

$$= \frac{\boxed{4 \cdot 7}}{5 \cdot 1} \quad \longleftarrow \quad \text{Multiply the numerators.}$$
$$\longleftarrow \quad \text{Multiply the denominators.}$$

$$= \boxed{\frac{28}{5}}, \text{ or } 5\boxed{\frac{3}{5}} \quad \text{Simplify.}$$

Your Turn Multiply. Write in simplest form.

a. $\frac{2}{7} \cdot \frac{5}{12}$

$$\boxed{\frac{5}{42}}$$

b. $-\frac{2}{15} \cdot \frac{5}{9}$

$$\boxed{-\frac{2}{27}}$$

c. $3\frac{2}{5} \cdot 2\frac{2}{9}$

$$\boxed{7\frac{5}{9}}$$

EXAMPLE Evaluate an Algebraic Expression

4 **ALGEBRA** Evaluate prq if $p = \frac{2}{3}$, $r = -\frac{4}{5}$, and $q = \frac{7}{8}$.

$$prq = \boxed{\frac{2}{3}} \cdot \boxed{-\frac{4}{5}} \cdot \boxed{\frac{7}{8}} \qquad \text{Replace } p \text{ with } \frac{2}{3}, r \text{ with } -\frac{4}{5}, \text{ and } q \text{ with } \frac{7}{8}.$$

$$= \frac{\overset{1}{\cancel{2}}}{3} \cdot -\frac{\overset{1}{\cancel{4}}}{5} \cdot \frac{7}{\underset{1}{\cancel{8}}} \qquad \text{Divide out common factors.}$$

$$= \frac{1 \cdot (-1) \cdot 7}{3 \cdot 5 \cdot 1} \text{ or } \boxed{-\frac{7}{15}} \qquad \text{Simplify.}$$

HOMEWORK ASSIGNMENT

Page(s):

Exercises:

Your Turn Evaluate prq if $p = -\frac{3}{4}$, $r = \frac{8}{9}$, and $q = \frac{1}{2}$.

$$\boxed{-\frac{1}{3}}$$

© Glencoe/McGraw-Hill

Dividing Rational Numbers

WHAT YOU'LL LEARN

- Divide fractions.

Two numbers whose product is one are **multiplicative inverses.**

The numbers 4 and $\frac{1}{4}$ are | **multiplicative inverses**

or **reciprocals** of each other.

KEY CONCEPTS

Inverse Property of Multiplication The product of a rational number and its multiplicative inverse is 1.

Dividing Fractions To divide by a fraction, multiply by its multiplicative inverse.

EXAMPLE Find a Multiplicative Inverse

1 Write the multiplicative inverse of $-2\frac{4}{7}$.

$-2\frac{4}{7} =$ | $-\dfrac{18}{7}$ | Write $-2\frac{4}{7}$, as an improper fraction.

Since $-\dfrac{18}{7}\left(-\dfrac{7}{18}\right) =$ | 1 |, the multiplicative inverse

of $-2\frac{4}{7}$ is | $-\dfrac{7}{18}$ |.

EXAMPLE Divide Fractions

2 Find $\dfrac{3}{10} \div \dfrac{2}{5}$. Write in simplest form.

$\dfrac{3}{10} \div \dfrac{2}{5} = \dfrac{3}{10} \cdot$ | $\dfrac{5}{2}$ | Multiply by the multiplicative inverse of $\frac{2}{5}$.

$= \dfrac{3}{\underset{2}{\cancel{10}}} \cdot \dfrac{\overset{1}{\cancel{5}}}{2}$ Divide 5 and 10 by their GCF, | 5 |.

$=$ | $\dfrac{3}{4}$ | Simplify.

Your Turn

a. Write the multiplicative inverse of $-1\frac{5}{6}$.

| $-\dfrac{6}{11}$ |

b. Find $\dfrac{4}{15} \div \dfrac{3}{5}$. Write in simplest form.

| $\dfrac{4}{9}$ |

FOLDABLES

ORGANIZE IT

On the tab for Lesson 2–4, explain in your own words how to divide rational numbers.

Algebra: Rational Numbers

EXAMPLE Divide by a Whole Number

3 Find $\frac{6}{7} \div 12$. Write in simplest form.

$$\frac{6}{7} \div 12 = \frac{6}{7} \div \frac{12}{1}$$

Write 12 as $\boxed{\dfrac{12}{1}}$.

$$= \frac{6}{7} \cdot \boxed{\dfrac{1}{12}}$$

Multiply by the multiplicative inverse of 12, which is $\boxed{\dfrac{1}{12}}$.

$$= \frac{\overset{1}{6}}{7} \cdot \frac{1}{\underset{2}{12}}$$

Divide 6 and 12 by their GCF, $\boxed{6}$.

$$= \boxed{\dfrac{1}{14}}$$

Simplify.

EXAMPLE Divide Negative Fractions

4 Find $\frac{2}{7} \div -\frac{8}{9}$. Write in simplest form.

$$\frac{2}{7} \div -\frac{8}{9} = \frac{2}{7} \cdot \boxed{-\dfrac{9}{8}}$$

Multiply by the multiplicative inverse of $-\frac{8}{9}$ which is $\boxed{-\dfrac{9}{8}}$.

$$= \frac{\overset{1}{2}}{7} \cdot -\frac{9}{\underset{4}{8}}$$

Divide 2 and 8 by their GCF, $\boxed{2}$.

$$= \boxed{-\dfrac{9}{28}}$$

The fractions have different signs, so the quotient is negative.

WRITE IT

Explain how you would divide a fraction by a whole number.

_____

_____

_____

_____

_____

Your Turn Find each quotient. Write in simplest form.

a. $\frac{3}{4} \div 6$

$\boxed{\dfrac{1}{8}}$

b. $-\frac{3}{5} \div \frac{9}{10}$

$\boxed{-\dfrac{2}{3}}$

EXAMPLE   Divide Mixed Numbers

5 Find $3\frac{1}{4} \div \left(-2\frac{1}{8}\right)$. Write in simplest form.

$$3\frac{1}{4} \div \left(-2\frac{1}{8}\right) = \boxed{\frac{13}{4}} \div \left(\boxed{-\frac{17}{8}}\right) \qquad 3\frac{1}{4} = \boxed{\frac{13}{4}},$$

$$-2\frac{1}{8} = \boxed{-\frac{17}{8}}$$

$$= \boxed{\frac{13}{4}} \cdot \left(-\frac{8}{17}\right) \qquad \text{The multiplicative}$$

inverse of $\boxed{-\frac{17}{8}}$

is $-\frac{8}{17}$.

$$= \frac{13}{\underset{1}{\cancel{4}}} \cdot \left(-\frac{\overset{2}{\cancel{8}}}{17}\right) \qquad \text{Divide 4 and 8 by their}$$

GCF, $\boxed{4}$.

$$= -\frac{26}{17} \text{ or } \boxed{-1\frac{9}{17}} \qquad \text{Simplify.}$$

Your Turn   Find $2\frac{1}{3} \div \left(-1\frac{1}{9}\right)$. Write in simplest form.

$$-2\frac{1}{10}$$

HOMEWORK ASSIGNMENT

Page(s): _____

Exercises: _____

_____

_____

Adding and Subtracting Like Fractions

WHAT YOU'LL LEARN

- Add and subtract fractions with like denominators

BUILD YOUR VOCABULARY (pages 32–33)

Fractions with like ⟨ **denominators** ⟩ are called **like fractions**.

EXAMPLE Add Like Fractions

1 Find $\frac{3}{16} + \left(-\frac{15}{16}\right)$. Write in simplest form.

$$\frac{3}{16} + \left(-\frac{15}{16}\right) = \frac{\boxed{3} + \left(\boxed{-15}\right)}{16} \quad\longleftarrow\quad \text{Add the numerators.}$$

$$\longleftarrow \text{The denominators are the same.}$$

$$= \frac{-12}{16} \text{ or } \boxed{-\frac{3}{4}} \qquad \text{Simplify.}$$

EXAMPLE Subtract Like Fractions

KEY CONCEPTS

Adding Like Fractions To add fractions with like denominators, add the numerators and write the sum over the denominator.

Subtracting Like Fractions To subtract fractions with like denominators, subtract the numerators and write the difference over the denominator.

2 Find $-\frac{7}{10} - \frac{9}{10}$. Write in simplest form.

$$-\frac{7}{10} - \frac{9}{10} = \frac{\boxed{-7 - 9}}{10} \quad\longleftarrow\quad \text{Subtract the numerators.}$$

$$\longleftarrow \text{The denominators are the same.}$$

$$= \frac{-16}{10} \text{ or } \boxed{-1\frac{3}{5}} \qquad \text{Rename } \frac{-16}{10} \text{ as } -1\frac{6}{10}$$

$$\text{or } \boxed{-1\frac{3}{5}}.$$

Your Turn Find each difference. Write in simplest form.

a. $\frac{2}{9} + \left(-\frac{8}{9}\right)$

$$-\frac{2}{3}$$

b. $-\frac{7}{8} - \frac{5}{8}$

$$-1\frac{1}{2}$$

ORGANIZE IT

Under the tab for Lesson 2–5, record models illustrating the addition and subtraction of like fractions.

Algebra:
Rational Numbers
2-1
2-2
2-3
2-4
2-5
2-6
2-7
2-8
2-9

EXAMPLE Add Mixed Numbers

③ Find $2\frac{5}{8} + 6\frac{1}{8}$. Write in simplest form.

$2\frac{5}{8} + 6\frac{1}{8} = \left(\boxed{2} + \boxed{6} \right) + \left(\frac{5}{8} + \frac{1}{8} \right)$ Add the whole numbers and fractions separately.

$= \boxed{8} + \frac{5+1}{8}$ Add the numerators.

$= \boxed{8\frac{6}{8}}$ or $\boxed{8\frac{3}{4}}$ Simplify.

EXAMPLE Subtract Mixed Numbers

④ **HEIGHTS** In the United States, the average height of a 9-year-old girl is $53\frac{4}{5}$ inches. The average height of a 16-year-old girl is $64\frac{1}{5}$ inches. How much does an average girl grow from age 9 to age 16?

$64\frac{1}{5} - 53\frac{4}{5} = \dfrac{\boxed{321}}{5} - \dfrac{\boxed{269}}{5}$ Write the mixed numbers as improper fractions.

$= \dfrac{\boxed{321} - \boxed{269}}{5}$ ← Subtract the numerators.
                ← The denominators are the same.

$= \frac{52}{5}$ or $\boxed{10\frac{2}{5}}$ Rename $\frac{52}{5}$ as $\boxed{10\frac{2}{5}}$.

The average girl grows $\boxed{10\frac{2}{5}}$ inches from age 9 to age 16.

Your Turn

a. Find $3\frac{3}{10} + 4\frac{1}{10}$. Write in simplest form.

$7\frac{2}{5}$

b. Ainsley was $42\frac{1}{7}$ inches tall when she was 4 years old. When she was 10 years old, she was $50\frac{3}{7}$ inches tall. How much did she grow between the ages of 4 and 10?

$8\frac{2}{7}$ inches

HOMEWORK ASSIGNMENT

Page(s): _____
Exercises: _____

_____

Adding and Subtracting Unlike Fractions

BUILD YOUR VOCABULARY (pages 32–33)

Fractions with unlike denominators are called **unlike fractions**.

EXAMPLE   Subtract Unlike Fractions

1 Find $\frac{1}{5} - \left(-\frac{2}{7}\right)$. **Write in simplest form.**

$$\frac{1}{5} - \left(-\frac{2}{7}\right) = \frac{1}{5} \cdot \frac{7}{7} - \left(-\frac{2}{7}\right) \cdot \frac{5}{5}$$

The LCD is $7 \cdot 5$ or 35 .

$$= \boxed{\frac{7}{35}} - \left(\boxed{-\frac{10}{35}}\right)$$

Rename each fraction using the LCD.

$$= \frac{7}{35} + \boxed{\frac{10}{35}}$$

Subtract $-\frac{10}{35}$ by adding its inverse, $\boxed{\frac{10}{35}}$.

$$= \frac{\boxed{7 + 10}}{35}$$

Add the numerators.

$$= \boxed{\frac{17}{35}}$$

Simplify.

Your Turn   Find $\frac{1}{3} - (-\frac{3}{5})$. Write in simplest form.

$\frac{14}{15}$

Mathematics: Applications and Concepts, Course 3

ORGANIZE IT

Under the tab for Lesson 2–6, record the differences between adding and subtracting like and unlike fractions.

Algebra:
Rational Numbers

EXAMPLE Add Mixed Numbers

② Find $-4\frac{1}{8} + 2\frac{5}{12}$. Write in simplest form.

$-4\frac{1}{8} + 2\frac{5}{12} = \boxed{-\frac{33}{8}} + \boxed{\frac{29}{12}}$ Write the mixed numbers as fractions.

$= -\frac{33}{8} \cdot \frac{3}{3} + \frac{29}{12} \cdot \frac{2}{2}$ The LCD is $2 \cdot 2 \cdot 2 \cdot 3$

or $\boxed{24}$.

$= -\boxed{\frac{99}{24}} + \boxed{\frac{58}{24}}$ Rename each fraction using the LCD.

$= \dfrac{\boxed{-99 + 58}}{24}$ Add the numerators.

$= \boxed{-\frac{41}{24}}$ or $1\boxed{\frac{17}{24}}$ Simplify.

Your Turn Find $-5\frac{1}{6} + 3\frac{5}{8}$. Write in simplest form.

$-1\frac{13}{24}$

EXAMPLE Evaluate Expressions
(parallels Example 4 in text)

③ ALGEBRA Find the value of $p - q$ if $p = \frac{2}{5}$ and $q = -\frac{4}{9}$.

$p - q = \frac{2}{5} - \left(-\frac{4}{9}\right)$ Replace p with $\frac{2}{5}$ and q with $-\frac{4}{9}$.

$= \boxed{\frac{18}{45}} - \left(-\frac{20}{45}\right)$ Rename each fraction using the LCD, $\boxed{45}$.

$= \dfrac{\boxed{18} + (-20)}{45}$ Subtract the numerators.

$= \boxed{\frac{38}{45}}$ Simplify.

Your Turn Find the value of $c - d$ if $c = \frac{3}{4}$ and $d = -\frac{8}{9}$.

$1\frac{23}{36}$

HOMEWORK ASSIGNMENT

Page(s):
Exercises:

Solving Equations with Rational Numbers

EXAMPLES Solve by Using Addition or Subtraction

WHAT YOU'LL LEARN

- Solve equations involving rational numbers.

1 Solve $g + 2.84 = 3.62$.

$$g + \boxed{2.84} = 3.62 \qquad \text{Write the equation.}$$

$$g + 2.84 - \boxed{2.84} = 3.62 - \boxed{2.84} \qquad \text{Subtract } \boxed{2.84}$$
from each side.

$$g = \boxed{0.78} \qquad \text{Simplify.}$$

FOLDABLES

ORGANIZE IT

Under the tab for Lesson 2–7, summarize in your own words what you have learned about solving equations with rational numbers.

2 Solve $-\dfrac{4}{5} = s - \dfrac{2}{3}$.

$$-\frac{4}{5} = s - \frac{2}{3} \qquad \text{Write the equation.}$$

$$-\frac{4}{5} + \boxed{\frac{2}{3}} = s - \frac{2}{3} + \boxed{\frac{2}{3}} \qquad \text{Add } \boxed{\frac{2}{3}} \text{ to each side.}$$

$$-\frac{4}{5} + \boxed{\frac{2}{3}} = s \qquad \text{Simplify.}$$

$$\boxed{-\frac{12}{15}} + \frac{10}{15} = s \qquad \text{Rename each fraction using the LCD.}$$

$$\boxed{-\frac{2}{15}} = s \qquad \text{Simplify.}$$

EXAMPLES Solve by Using Multiplication or Division

3 Solve $\dfrac{7}{11}c = -21$.

$$\frac{7}{11}c = -21 \qquad \text{Write the equation.}$$

$$\boxed{\frac{11}{7}}\left(\frac{7}{11}c\right) = \boxed{\frac{11}{7}}(-21) \qquad \text{Multiply each side by } \boxed{\frac{11}{7}}.$$

$$c = \boxed{-33} \qquad \text{Simplify.}$$

REVIEW IT

What is a mathematical sentence containing equals sign called? (*Lesson 1–8*)

_____

_____

_____

_____

4 Solve $9.7t = -67.9$.

$9.7t = -67.9$ Write the equation.

$\dfrac{9.7t}{\boxed{9.7}} = \dfrac{-67.9}{\boxed{9.7}}$ Divide each side by $\boxed{9.7}$.

$t = \boxed{-7}$ Simplify.

Your Turn Solve each equation.

a. $h + 2.65 = 5.73$

$\boxed{3.08}$

b. $-\dfrac{2}{5} = x - \dfrac{3}{4}$.

$\boxed{\dfrac{7}{20}}$

c. $\dfrac{3}{5}x = -27$

$\boxed{-45}$

d. $3.4t = -27.2$

$\boxed{-8}$

EXAMPLE Write an Equation to Solve a Problem

5 **PHYSICS** You can determine the rate an object is traveling by dividing the distance it travels by the time it takes to cover the distance $\left(r = \dfrac{d}{t}\right)$. If an object travels at a rate of 14.3 meters per second for 17 seconds, how far does it travel?

$r = \dfrac{d}{t}$

$14.3 = \dfrac{d}{\boxed{17}}$ Write the equation.

$\boxed{17}(14.3) = 17\left(\dfrac{d}{\boxed{17}}\right)$ Multiply each side by $\boxed{17}$.

$\boxed{243.1} = d$ Simplify.

Your Turn If an object travels at a rate of 73 miles per hour for 5.2 hours, how far does it travel?

$\boxed{379.6 \text{ miles}}$

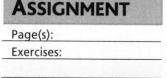

HOMEWORK ASSIGNMENT

Page(s): _____

Exercises: _____

_____

WHAT YOU'LL LEARN

- Use powers and exponents in expressions.

BUILD YOUR VOCABULARY (pages 32–33)

The **base** is the number that is | multiplied |.

The **exponent** tells how many times the | base | is used

as a | factor |.

The number that is expressed using an | exponent | is

called a **power**.

KEY CONCEPTS

Zero and Negative Exponents Any nonzero number to the zero power is 1. Any nonzero number to the negative n power is 1 divided by the number to the nth power.

EXAMPLE Write an Expression Using Powers

1 Write $p \cdot p \cdot p \cdot q \cdot p \cdot q \cdot q$ using exponents.

$p \cdot p \cdot p \cdot q \cdot p \cdot q \cdot q$

$= p \cdot p \cdot p \cdot p \cdot q \cdot q \cdot q$ | **Commutative** | Property

$= (p \cdot p \cdot p \cdot p) \cdot (q \cdot q \cdot q)$ | **Associative** | Property

$= $ | p^4 | $\cdot$ | q^3 | Definition of exponents

Your Turn Write $x \cdot y \cdot x \cdot x \cdot y \cdot y \cdot y$ using exponents.

$x^3 y^4$

EXAMPLES Evaluate Powers

2 Evaluate 9^5.

$9^5 = $ | $9 \cdot 9 \cdot 9 \cdot 9 \cdot 9$ | Definition of exponents

$= 59,049$ Simplify.

Check using a calculator.

9 $\boxed{\wedge}$ 5 $\boxed{\text{ENTER}}$ | **59049**

ORGANIZE IT

On the tab for Lesson 2–8, compare how to evaluate an expression with positive exponents and one with negative exponents.

3 Evaluate 3^{-7}.

$3^{-7} = \dfrac{1}{\boxed{3^7}}$ Definition of exponents

$= \dfrac{1}{\boxed{2,187}}$ Simplify.

4 **ALGEBRA** Evaluate $x^3 \cdot y^5$ if $x = 4$ and $y = 2$.

$x^3 \cdot y^5 = \boxed{4}^3 \cdot \boxed{2}^5$ Replace x with $\boxed{4}$ and y with $\boxed{2}$.

$= \left(\boxed{4 \cdot 4 \cdot 4} \right) \cdot \left(\boxed{2 \cdot 2 \cdot 2 \cdot 2 \cdot 2} \right)$

     Definition of exponents

$= 64 \cdot 32$ Simplify.

$= \boxed{2,048}$ Simplify.

Your Turn Evaluate each expression.

a. 6^5

7,776

b. 2^{-5}

$\dfrac{1}{32}$

c. Evaluate $x^2 \cdot y^4$ if $x = 3$ and $y = 4$.

2,304

HOMEWORK ASSIGNMENT

Page(s):

Exercises:

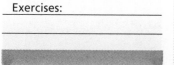

- Express numbers in scientific notation.

BUILD YOUR VOCABULARY (pages 32–33)

A number is expressed in **scientific notation** when it is written as a **product** of a factor and a **power** of 10.

KEY CONCEPT

Scientific Notation A number is expressed in scientific notation when it is written as the product of a factor and a power of 10. The factor must be greater than or equal to 1 and less than 10.

EXAMPLES Express Numbers in Standard Form

1 Write 9.62×10^5 in standard form.

$9.62 \times 10^5 = 9.62 \times \boxed{100,000}$

$= 962000$

$= \boxed{962,000}$

$10^5 = 10 \cdot 10 \cdot 10 \cdot 10 \cdot 10$

or $\boxed{100,000}$

Notice that the decimal place moves $\boxed{5}$ places to the right.

2 Write 2.85×10^{-6} in standard form.

$2.85 \times 10^{-6} = 2.85 \times \boxed{\dfrac{1}{10^6}}$

$= 2.85 \times 0.000001$

$= 0.00000285$

$= \boxed{0.00000285}$

$10^{-6} = \boxed{\dfrac{1}{10^6}}$

Notice that the decimal point moves 6 places to the left.

Your Turn Write each number in standard form.

a. 5.32×10^4

$\boxed{53,200}$

b. 3.81×10^{-4}

$\boxed{0.000381}$

FOLDABLES™

ORGANIZE IT

Under the tab for Lesson 2–9, collect and record examples of numbers you encounter in your daily life and write them in scientific notation.

EXAMPLES Write Numbers in Scientific Notation

3 Write 931,500,000 in scientific notation.

$931500000 = 9.315 \times 100{,}000{,}000$ — The decimal point moves 8 places.

$= \boxed{9.315 \times 10^8}$ — The exponent is positive.

4 Write 0.00443 in scientific notation.

$0.00443 = \boxed{4.43} \times 0.001$ — The decimal point moves

$\boxed{3}$ places.

$= 4.43 \times \boxed{10^{-3}}$ — The exponent is $\boxed{\text{negative}}$.

EXAMPLE Compare Numbers in Scientific Notation

5 PLANETS The following table lists the average radius at the equator for each of the planets in our solar system. Order the planets according to radius from largest to smallest.

First order the numbers according to their exponents. Then order the numbers with the same exponents by comparing the factors.

Planet	Radius (km)
Earth	6.38×10^3
Jupiter	7.14×10^4
Mars	3.40×10^3
Mercury	2.44×10^3
Neptune	2.43×10^4
Pluto	1.5×10^3
Saturn	6.0×10^4
Uranus	2.54×10^4
Venus	6.05×10^3

Source: *CRC Handbook of Chemistry and Physics*

STEP 2

$$7.14 \times 10^4 > 6.0 \times 10^4 > 2.54 \times 10^4 > 2.43 \times 10^4$$

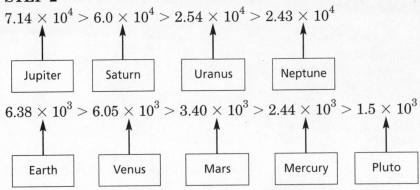

| Jupiter | Saturn | Uranus | Neptune |

$$6.38 \times 10^3 > 6.05 \times 10^3 > 3.40 \times 10^3 > 2.44 \times 10^3 > 1.5 \times 10^3$$

| Earth | Venus | Mars | Mercury | Pluto |

The order from largest to smallest is **Jupiter**, Saturn,

Uranus, Neptune, Earth, Venus, Mars, Mercury, and **Pluto**.

Your Turn Write each number in scientific notation.

a. 35,600,000

$$3.56 \times 10^7$$

b. 0.000653

$$6.53 \times 10^{-4}$$

c. The following table lists the mass for each of the planets in our solar system. Order the planets according to mass from largest to smallest.

Planet	Mass (in tons)
Mercury	3.64×10^{20}
Venus	5.37×10^{21}
Earth	6.58×10^{21}
Mars	7.08×10^{20}
Jupiter	2.09×10^{24}
Saturn	6.25×10^{23}
Uranus	9.57×10^{22}
Neptune	1.13×10^{23}
Pluto	1.38×10^{19}

Source: nssdc.gsfc.nasa.gov

Jupiter, Saturn, Neptune, Uranus, Earth, Venus, Mars, Mercury, and Pluto

HOMEWORK ASSIGNMENT

Page(s): _____

Exercises: _____

_____

_____

FOLDABLES	**VOCABULARY PUZZLEMAKER**	**BUILD YOUR VOCABULARY**
Use your **Chapter 2 Foldable** to help you study for your chapter test.	To make a crossword puzzle, word search, or jumble puzzle of the vocabulary words in Chapter 2, go to: www.glencoe.com/sec/math/ t_resources/free/index.php	You can use your completed **Vocabulary Builder** (*pages 32–33*) to help you solve the puzzle.

2-1
Fractions and Decimals

Write each fraction or mixed number as a decimal.

1. $-\dfrac{3}{4}$

$$-.75$$

2. $3\dfrac{1}{6}$

$$3.83$$

3. $-7\dfrac{2}{5}$

$$-7.4$$

Write each decimal as a fraction or mixed number in simplest form.

4. 9.5

$$9\dfrac{1}{2}$$

5. 0.6

$$\dfrac{2}{3}$$

6. 8.125

$$8\dfrac{1}{8}$$

2-2
Comparing and Ordering Rational Numbers

Use < , > or = to make each sentence true.

7. $-\dfrac{4}{5}$ $\boxed{<}$ $-\dfrac{2}{3}$

8. 4.4 $\boxed{=}$ $4\dfrac{2}{5}$

9. 2.93 $\boxed{=}$ 2.93

Graph each pair of rational numbers on a number line.

10. $\dfrac{1}{5}, \dfrac{1}{3}$

11. $-\dfrac{4}{5}, -\dfrac{9}{10}$

2-3

Multiplying Rational Numbers

Complete each sentence.

12. The greatest common factor of two numbers is the

$\boxed{\textbf{largest}}$ number that is a $\boxed{\textbf{factor}}$ of both numbers.

13. Numerators and denominators are $\boxed{\textbf{divided}}$ by their

greatest common factors to $\boxed{\textbf{simplify}}$ the product.

Multiply. Write in simplest form.

14. $-\dfrac{7}{12} \cdot \dfrac{3}{4}$

$\boxed{-\dfrac{21}{48}; -\dfrac{7}{16}}$

15. $4\dfrac{2}{3} \cdot 5\dfrac{1}{8}$

$\boxed{\dfrac{287}{12}; 23\dfrac{11}{12}}$

2-4

Dividing Rational Numbers

Write the multiplicative inverse for each mixed number.

16. $2\dfrac{1}{5}$ $\boxed{\dfrac{5}{11}}$ **17.** $-1\dfrac{3}{8}$ $\boxed{-\dfrac{8}{11}}$ **18.** $3\dfrac{4}{7}$ $\boxed{\dfrac{7}{25}}$

Complete the sentence.

19. To divide by a $\boxed{\textbf{fraction}}$, multiply by its

$\boxed{\textbf{multiplicative}}$ inverse.

20. To $\boxed{\textbf{divide}}$ a number by $2\dfrac{1}{5}$, multiply by $\dfrac{5}{11}$.

2-5

Adding and Subtracting Like Fractions

Determine whether each pair of fractions are like fractions.

21. $\dfrac{3}{5}, \dfrac{3}{7}$ $\boxed{\textbf{no}}$ **22.** $\dfrac{5}{8}, \dfrac{7}{8}$ $\boxed{\textbf{yes}}$ **23.** $\dfrac{4}{7}, -\dfrac{5}{7}$ $\boxed{\textbf{yes}}$ **24.** $\dfrac{5}{9}, -\dfrac{2}{3}$ $\boxed{\textbf{no}}$

Add or subtract. Write in simplest form.

25. $\dfrac{5}{9} - \dfrac{2}{9}$ $\boxed{\dfrac{1}{3}}$ **26.** $\dfrac{5}{8} + \dfrac{7}{8}$ $\boxed{1\dfrac{1}{2}}$ **27.** $\dfrac{4}{7} - \dfrac{5}{7}$ $\boxed{-\dfrac{1}{7}}$

2-6

Adding and Subtracting Unlike Fractions

Find the LCD.

28. $\frac{3}{5}, \frac{3}{7}$ | **35**   **29.** $\frac{5}{8}, \frac{7}{12}$ | **24**   **30.** $\frac{5}{9}, \frac{-2}{3}$ | **9**

Add or subtract. Write in simplest form.

31. $\frac{5}{8} - \frac{7}{12}$ **32.** $\frac{3}{5} + \frac{3}{7}$

$\frac{1}{24}$ $1\frac{1}{35}$

2-7

Solving Equations with Rational Numbers

Match the method of solving with the appropriate equation.

33. $25a = 3.75$ | **c**   **a.** Subtract $\frac{3}{5}$ from each side

34. $\frac{3}{5}m + \frac{7}{10}$ | **b**   **b.** Multiply each side by $\frac{5}{3}$

35. $r - 1.25 = 4.5$ | **d**   **c.** Subtract 3.75 from each side

36. $\frac{3}{5} + f = \frac{1}{2}$ | **a**   **d.** Add 1.25 to each side

e. Divide each side by 1.25

2-8

Powers and Exponents

Identify the base, exponent, and power of each expression.

37. 5^4 **base: 5; exponent: 4; power: 5^4**

38. x^8 **base: x; exponent: 8; power: x^8**

Evaluate each expression.

38. 5^4 | **625**   **40.** 6^3 | **216**   **41.** 2^8 | **256**

2-9

Scientific Notation

Write each number in scientific notation.

42. 8,790,000 | **8.79×10^6**   **43.** 0.0000125 | **1.25×10^{-5}**

44. 0.00899 | **8.99×10^{-3}**   **45.** 402,500,000 | **4.025×10^8**

CHAPTER 2 Checklist

ARE YOU READY FOR THE CHAPTER TEST?

Visit **msmath3.net** to access your textbook, more examples, self-check quizzes, and practice tests to help you study the concepts in Chapter 2.

Check the one that applies. Suggestions to help you study are given with each item.

☐ **I completed the review of all or most lessons without using my notes or asking for help.**

- You are probably ready for the Chapter Test.
- You may want take the Chapter 2 Practice Test on page 111 of your textbook as a final check.

☐ **I used my Foldable or Study Notebook to complete the review of all or most lessons.**

- You should complete the Chapter 2 Study Guide and Review on pages 108–110 of your textbook.
- If you are unsure of any concepts or skills, refer back to the specific lesson(s).
- You may also want to take the Chapter 2 Practice Test on page 111 of your text book.

☐ **I asked for help from someone else to complete the review of all or most lessons.**

- You should review the examples and concepts in your Study Notebook and Chapter 2 Foldable.
- Then complete the Chapter 2 Study Guide and Review on pages 108–110 of your textbook.
- If you are unsure of any concepts or skills, refer back to the specific lesson(s).
- You may also want to take the Chapter 2 Practice Test on page 111 of your textbook.

Student Signature   Parent/Guardian Signature

Teacher Signature

Algebra: Real Numbers and the Pythagorean Theorem

 Use the instructions below to make a Foldable to help you organize your notes as you study the chapter. You will see Foldable reminders in the margin of this Interactive Study Notebook to help you in taking notes.

Begin with two sheets of $8\frac{1}{2}$" by 11" paper.

STEP 1 **Fold and Cut One Sheet**
Fold in half from top to bottom. Cut along fold from edges to margin.

STEP 2 **Fold and Cut the Other Sheet**
Fold in half from top to bottom. Cut along fold between margins.

STEP 3 **Assemble**
Insert first sheet through second sheet and align folds.

STEP 4 **Label**
Label each page with a lesson number and title.

Chapter 3
Algebra: Real
Numbers and the
Pythagorean
Theorem

 NOTE-TAKING TIP: When you take notes, clarify terms, record concepts, and write examples for each lesson. You may also want to list ways in which the new concepts can be used in your daily life.

Chapter 3

CHAPTER 3

This is an alphabetical list of new vocabulary terms you will learn in Chapter 3. As you complete the study notes for the chapter, you will see Build Your Vocabulary reminders to complete each term's definition or description on these pages. Remember to add the textbook page number in the second column for reference when you study.

Vocabulary Term	Found on Page	Definition	Description or Example
abscissa [ab-SIH-suh]			
converse			
coordinate plane			
hypotenuse			
irrational number			
legs			
ordered pair			
ordinate [OR-din-it]			
origin			
perfect square			

© Glencoe/McGraw-Hill

Vocabulary Term	Found on Page	Definition	Description or Example
principal square root			
Pythagorean Theorem			
Pythagorean triple			
quadrants			
radical sign			
real number			
right triangle			
square root			
x-axis			
x-coordinate			
y-axis			
y-coordinate			

3-1 Square Roots

WHAT YOU'LL LEARN

- Find square roots of perfect squares.

BUILD YOUR VOCABULARY (pages 60–61)

Numbers such as 1, 4, 9, and 25 are called **perfect squares** because they are squares of   whole   numbers.

The   opposite   of squaring a number is finding a **square root**.

The symbol $\sqrt{}$ is called a **radical sign** and is used to indicate the positive   square root .

A   positive   square root is called the **principal square root**.

EXAMPLE Find a Square Root

KEY CONCEPT

Square Root A square root of a number is one of its two equal factors.

1 Find $\sqrt{81}$.

$\sqrt{81}$ indicates the   positive   square root of 81.

Since 9^2 = 81, $\sqrt{81}$ =   9 .

EXAMPLE Find the Negative Square Root

2 Find $-\sqrt{144}$.

$-\sqrt{144}$ indicates the   negative   square root of 144.

Since (-12) (−12)   = 144, $-\sqrt{144}$ =   −12 .

Your Turn Find each square root.

a. $\sqrt{64}$ 8

b. 36   −6

EXAMPLE Use Square Roots to Solve an Equation

3 ALGEBRA Solve $x^2 = \frac{49}{64}$.

$x^2 = \frac{49}{64}$ — Write the equation.

$\sqrt{x^2} = \sqrt{\frac{49}{64}}$ or $\boxed{-\sqrt{\frac{49}{64}}}$ — Take the square root of each side.

$x = \boxed{\frac{7}{8}}$ or $-\frac{7}{8}$ — Notice that $\frac{7}{8} \cdot \frac{7}{8} = \boxed{\frac{49}{64}}$ and

$\left(-\frac{7}{8}\right)\left(-\frac{7}{8}\right) = \boxed{\frac{49}{64}}$.

The equation has two solutions, $\boxed{\frac{7}{8}}$ and $\boxed{-\frac{7}{8}}$.

FOLDABLES

ORGANIZE IT
On Lesson 3-1 of your Foldable, explain how to find the square root of a number and give an example.

Chapter 3
Algebra: Real Numbers and the Pythagorean Theorem

Your Turn Solve $x^2 = \frac{81}{100}$.

$\frac{9}{10}, \frac{9}{10}$

EXAMPLE Use an Equation to Solve a Problem

4 MUSIC The art work of the square picture in a compact disc case is approximately 14,161 mm² in area. Find the length of each side of the square.

The area is equal to the square of the length of a side.
Let A = the area and let s = the length of the side $A = s^2$

$14,161 = s^2$ — Write the equation.

$\boxed{\sqrt{14,161}} = \sqrt{s^2}$ — Take the square root of each side.

The length of a side of a compact disc case is about $\boxed{119}$ millimeters since distance cannot be negative.

Your Turn A piece of art is a square picture that is approximately 11,025 square inches in area. Find the length of each side of the square picture.

105 inches

HOMEWORK ASSIGNMENT
Page(s):
Exercises:

Estimating Square Roots

WHAT YOU'LL LEARN
- Estimate square roots.

EXAMPLE Estimate Square Roots

1 **Estimate $\sqrt{54}$ to the nearest whole number.**

The first perfect square less than 54 is 　49　.

The first perfect square greater than 54 is 　64　.

$49 < 54 < 64$　　　Write an inequality.

$\boxed{7^2} < 54 < \boxed{8^2}$　　$49 = \boxed{7^2}$ and $64 = \boxed{8^2}$

$\sqrt{7^2} < \sqrt{54} < \sqrt{8^2}$　　Take the square root of each number.

$7 < \sqrt{54} < 8$　　Simplify.

So, $\sqrt{54}$ is between 　7　 and 　8　. Since 54 is closer to 49 than 64, the best whole number estimate for $\sqrt{54}$ is 　7　.

EXAMPLE Estimate Square Roots

FOLDABLES

ORGANIZE IT
On Lesson 3-2 of your Foldable, explain how to estimate square roots.

Chapter 3
Algebra: Real Numbers and the Pythagorean Theorem

2 **FINANCE** If you were to invest $100 in a bank account for two years, your money would earn interest daily and be worth more when you withdrew it. If you had $120 after two years, the interest rate, written as a decimal, would be found using the expression $\frac{(\sqrt{120} - 10)}{10}$. Estimate this value.

First estimate the value of $\sqrt{120}$.

$100 < 120 < 121$　　　$\boxed{100}$ and $\boxed{121}$ are perfect squares.

$10^2 < 120 < 11^2$　　$100 = \boxed{10^2}$ and $121 = \boxed{11^2}$

$\boxed{10} < \sqrt{120} < \boxed{11}$　　Take the square root of each number.

Since 120 is closer to $\boxed{121}$ than 100, the best whole

number estimate for $\sqrt{120}$ is $\boxed{11}$. Use this to evaluate
the expression.

$$\frac{(\sqrt{120} - 10)}{10} = \frac{(\boxed{11} - 10)}{10} \text{ or } \boxed{0.10}$$

The approximate interest rate is 0.10 or $\boxed{10\%}$.

Your Turn

a. Estimate $\sqrt{65}$ to the nearest whole number.

8

b. If you were to invest $100 in a bank account for two years, your money would earn interest daily and be worth more when you withdrew it. If you had $250 after two years, the interest rate, written as a decimal, would be found using the expression $\frac{(\sqrt{150} - 10)}{10}$.

0.20 or 20%

HOMEWORK ASSIGNMENT

Page(s):

Exercises:

The Real Number System

WHAT YOU'LL LEARN

- Identify and classify numbers in the real number system.

BUILD YOUR VOCABULARY (pages 60–61)

Numbers that are not [**rational**] are called **irrational numbers**.

The set of rational numbers and the set of [**rational**] numbers together make up the set of **real numbers**.

KEY CONCEPT

Irrational Number An irrational number is a number that cannot be expressed as $\frac{a}{b}$, where a and b are integers and $b \neq 0$.

EXAMPLES Classify Numbers

Name all sets of numbers to which each real number belongs.

1 $\sqrt{25}$

Since $\sqrt{25} =$ [**5**], it is a [**whole**] number, an [**integer**], and a rational number.

2 $-\sqrt{12}$

Since the decimal does not repeat or [**terminate**], it is an [**irrational**] number.

3 $0.090909\ldots$

The decimal ends in a [**repeating**] pattern.

It is a [**rational**] number because it is equivalent to $\boxed{\dfrac{1}{11}}$.

Your Turn **Name all sets of numbers to which each real number belongs.**

a. $\sqrt{64}$ [**whole, integer, rational**]

b. $0.1010101010\ldots$ [**rational**]

c. $\sqrt{13}$ [**irrational**]

ORGANIZE IT

On Lesson 3-3 of your Foldable, summarize the properties of the real number system.

EXAMPLE Graph Real Numbers

4 Estimate $\sqrt{8}$ and $-\sqrt{2}$ to the nearest tenth. Then graph $\sqrt{8}$ and $-\sqrt{2}$ on a number line.

Use a calculator to determine the approximate decimal values.

$\sqrt{8} \approx$ **2.828427125 . . .**

$-\sqrt{2} \approx$ **−1.414213562 . . .**

Locate these points on a number line.

$\sqrt{8} \approx$ **2.8** and $-\sqrt{2} \approx$ **−1.4** .

Your Turn Estimate $\sqrt{3}$ and $-\sqrt{6}$ to the nearest tenth. Then graph $\sqrt{3}$ and $-\sqrt{6}$ on a number line.

$\sqrt{3} \approx 1.7, -\sqrt{6} \approx -2.4$

EXAMPLES Compare Real Numbers

REMEMBER IT

Always simplify numbers before classifying them.

5 Replace each ● with <, >, or = to make a true sentence.

$3\frac{7}{8}$ ● $\sqrt{15}$

Write each number as a decimal.

$3\frac{7}{8} =$ **3.875** $\qquad$ $\sqrt{15} =$ **3.872983346 . . .**

Since **3.875** is greater than **3.872983346 . . .** ,

$3\frac{7}{8}$ **>** $\sqrt{15}$.

WRITE IT

Explain why you can determine that $-\sqrt{2}$ is less than 1.2 without computation.

_____

_____

_____

_____

_____

_____

6 $3.\overline{2}$ ● $\sqrt{10.4}$

Write $\sqrt{10.4}$ as a decimal.

$\sqrt{10.4} \approx$ **3.224903099**

Since $3.\overline{2}$ is **less** than 3.224903099 . . . ,

$3.\overline{2}$ **<** $\sqrt{10.4}$.

Your Turn Replace each ● with <, >, or = to make a true sentence.

a. $3\frac{3}{8}$ ● $\sqrt{14}$

$$3\frac{3}{8} > \sqrt{14}$$

b. $1.\overline{5}$ ● $\sqrt{2.25}$

$$1.\overline{5} > \sqrt{2.25}$$

EXAMPLE

7 **BASEBALL** The time in seconds that it takes an object to fall d feet is $0.25\sqrt{d}$. How many seconds would it take for a baseball that is hit 250 feet straight up in the air to fall from its highest point to the ground?

Use a calculator to approximate the time it will take for the baseball to fall to the ground.

$0.25\sqrt{d} = 0.25$ $\sqrt{250}$ Replace d with **250**.

≈ 3.95 or about **4**   Use a calculator.

It will take about **4 seconds** for the baseball to fall to the ground.

Your Turn The time in seconds that it takes an object to fall d feet is $0.25\sqrt{d}$. How many seconds would it take for a baseball that is hit 450 feet straight up in the air to fall from its highest point to the ground?

about 5 seconds

HOMEWORK ASSIGNMENT

Page(s): _____

Exercises: _____

_____

_____

The Pythagorean Theorem

WHAT YOU'LL LEARN

• Use the Pythagorean Theorem.

BUILD YOUR VOCABULARY (pages 60–61)

A **right triangle** is a triangle with one right angle of 90°.

The sides that form the right angle are called **legs**.

The **hypotenuse** is the side opposite the right angle.

The **Pythagorean Theorem** describes the relationship between the lengths of the legs and the hypotenuse for *any* right triangle.

KEY CONCEPT

Pythagorean Theorem In a right triangle, the square of the length of the hypotenuse is equal to the sum of the squares of the lengths of the legs.

EXAMPLE   Find the Length of the Hypotenuse

1 **KITES** Find the length of the kite string.

The kite string forms the hypotenuse of a right triangle. The vertical and horizontal distances form the legs.

$c^2 = a^2 + b^2$ Pythagorean Theorem

$c^2 = 5^2 + \boxed{12^2}$ Replace a with $\boxed{5}$ and

 b with $\boxed{12}$.

$c^2 = \boxed{25} + \boxed{144}$ Evaluate 5^2 and 12^2.

$c^2 = \boxed{169}$ Add $\boxed{25}$ and 144.

$\sqrt{c^2} = \sqrt{169}$ Take the square root of each side.

$c = \boxed{13}$ or $\boxed{-13}$ Simplify.

The equation has two solutions, $\boxed{13}$ and $\boxed{-13}$.

However, the length of the kite string must be positive.

The kite string is $\boxed{13}$ feet long.

Your Turn Find the length of the kite string.

> 26 ft

c ft   24 ft

10 ft

EXAMPLE Find the Length of a Leg

ORGANIZE IT

On Lesson 3-4 of your Foldable, explain how to use the Pythagorean Theorem to find the missing length of a side of a right triangle.

Chapter 3
Algebra: Real Numbers and the Pythagorean Theorem

2 The hypotenuse of a right triangle is 33 centimeters long and one of its legs is 28 centimeters. Find the length of the other leg.

$$c^2 = a^2 + b^2$$ Pythagorean Theorem

$$\boxed{33}^2 = a^2 + \boxed{28}^2$$ Replace the variables.

$$1{,}089 = a^2 + 784$$ Evaluate each power.

$$\boxed{1{,}089} - \boxed{784} = a^2 + \boxed{784} - \boxed{784}$$ Subtract.

$$\boxed{305} = a^2$$ Simplify.

$$\sqrt{305} = \sqrt{a^2}$$ Take the square root of each side.

$$\boxed{17.5} \approx a$$ Use a calculator.

The length of the other leg is about $\boxed{17.5}$ centimeters.

Your Turn The hypotenuse of a right triangle is 26 centimeters long and one of its legs is 17 centimeters. Find the length of the other leg.

> about 19.7 cm

REMEMBER IT

The longest side of a right triangle is the hypotenuse. Therefore, *c* represents the length of the longest side.

EXAMPLE Use the Pythagorean Theorem

3 A 10-foot ramp is extended from the back of a truck to the ground to help movers load furniture onto the truck. If the ramp touches the ground at a point 9 feet behind the truck, how high off the ground is the top of the ramp?

10 ft

9 ft

$$c^2 = a^2 + b^2$$ Pythagorean Theorem

$$10^2 = a^2 + 9^2$$ Replace c with 10 and b with 9.

$$\boxed{100} = a^2 + \boxed{81}$$ Evaluate each power.

$$\boxed{100} - 81 = a^2 + \boxed{81} - 81$$ Subtract 81 from each side.

$$19 = a^2$$ Simplify.

$$\boxed{\sqrt{19}} = \sqrt{a^2}$$ Take the square root of each side.

$$\boxed{4.4} \approx a$$ Simplify.

The top of the ramp is $\boxed{4.4}$ feet off the ground.

KEY CONCEPT

Converse of the Pythagorean Theorem If the sides of a triangle have lengths a, b, and c units such that $c^2 = a^2 + b^2$, then the triangle is a right triangle.

EXAMPLE Identify a Right Triangle

4 **The measures of three sides of a triangle are 24 inches, 7 inches, and 25 inches. Determine whether the triangle is a right triangle.**

$$c^2 = a^2 + b^2$$ Pythagorean Theorem

$$25^2 \stackrel{?}{=} 7^2 + 24^2$$ $c = 25$, $a = 7$, $b = 24$

$$625 \stackrel{?}{=} \boxed{49} + 576$$ Evaluate 25^2, 7^2, and 24^2.

$$\boxed{625} = 625$$ Simplify. The triangle is a right triangle.

Your Turn

a. The base of a 12-foot ladder is 5 feet from the wall. How high can the ladder reach?

about 10.9 feet

b. The measures of three sides of a triangle are 13 inches, 5 inches, and 12 inches. Determine whether the triangle is a right triangle.

yes

HOMEWORK ASSIGNMENT

Page(s):

Exercises:

© Glencoe/McGraw-Hill

Using the Pythagorean Theorem

© Glencoe/McGraw-Hill

EXAMPLE Use the Pythagorean Theorem

WHAT YOU'LL LEARN

- Solve problems using the Pythagorean Theorem.

1 RAMPS A ramp to the entrance of a newly constructed building must be built according to accessibility guidelines stated in the Americans with Disabilities Act. If the ramp is 24.1 feet long and the top of the ramp is 2 feet off the ground, how far is the end of the ramp from the entrance?

Notice the problem involves a right triangle. Use the Pythagorean Theorem.

$$24.1^2 = a^2 + 2^2 \qquad \text{Write the equation.}$$

$$\boxed{580.81} = a^2 + \boxed{4} \qquad \text{Evaluate } 24.1^2 \text{ and } 2^2.$$

$$\boxed{580.81} - \boxed{4} = a^2 + \boxed{4} - \boxed{4} \qquad \text{Subtract } \boxed{4} \text{ from each side.}$$

$$\boxed{576.81} = a^2 \qquad \text{Simplify.}$$

$$\boxed{\sqrt{576.81}} = \sqrt{a^2} \qquad \text{Take the square root of each side.}$$

$$\boxed{24.0} \approx a \qquad \text{Simplify.}$$

The end of the ramp is about $\boxed{24 \text{ feet}}$ from the entrance.

FOLDABLES

ORGANIZE IT

On Lesson 3-5 of your Foldable, explain the Pythagorean Theorem in your own words and give an example of how it might be used in a real-life situation.

Chapter 3
Algebra: Real Numbers and the Pythagorean Theorem

Your Turn If a truck ramp is 32 feet long and the top of the ramp is 10 feet off the ground, how far is the end of the ramp from the truck?

about 30.4 feet

BUILD YOUR VOCABULARY (pages 60–61)

Whole numbers such as 3, 4, and 5, which satisfy the

Pythagorean Theorem , are called

Pythagorean triples.

EXAMPLE Write Pythagorean Triples

2 **Multiply the triple 5-12-13 by the numbers 2, 3, 4, 5, and 10 to find more Pythagorean triples.**

You can use a table to organize your answers. Multiply each Pythagorean triple entry by the same number.

	a	*b*	*c*
original	5	12	13
× 2	10	24	26
× 3	15	36	39
× 4	20	48	52
× 5	25	60	65
× 10	50	120	130

Each triple listed in the table is a Pythagorean triple. To verify, you can use the Pythagorean Theorem to show that each triple satisfies the equation.

Your Turn Multiply the triple 8-15-17 by the numbers 2, 3, 4, and 10 to find more Pythagorean triples.

16, 30, 34; 24, 45, 51; 32, 60, 68; 80, 150, 170

HOMEWORK ASSIGNMENT

Page(s): _____

Exercises: _____

_____

_____

Distance on the Coordinate Plane

WHAT YOU'LL LEARN

- Find the distance between points on the coordinate plane.

BUILD YOUR VOCABULARY (pages 60–61)

A **coordinate plane** is formed by two number lines that form right angles and intersect at their | zero | points.

The point of intersection of the two number lines is the **origin**.

The | vertical | number line is the **y-axis**.

The | horizontal | number line is the **x-axis**.

The number lines separate the coordinate plane into

| four | sections called **quadrants**.

Any point on the coordinate plane can be graphed by using an **ordered pair** of numbers.

The | first | number in the ordered pair is called the

x-coordinate.

The | second | number of an ordered pair is the

y-coordinate.

Another name for the | **x-coordinate** | is **abscissa**.

Another name for the | **y-coordinate** | is **ordinate**.

FOLDABLES

ORGANIZE IT

On Lesson 3-6 of your Foldable, explain in writing how to use ordered pairs to find the distance between two points.

Chapter 3
Algebra: Real Numbers and the Pythagorean Theorem

EXAMPLE Find the Distance on the Coordinate Plane

① Graph the ordered pairs (0, −6) and (5, −1). Then find the distance between the points.

Mathematics: Applications and Concepts, Course 3

Let c = distance between the two points, $a = 5$, and $b = 5$.

$c^2 = a^2 + b^2$ Pythagorean Theorem

$c^2 = \boxed{5^2} + \boxed{5^2}$ Replace a with $\boxed{5}$ and b with $\boxed{5}$.

$c^2 = \boxed{25} + \boxed{25}$ Evaluate $\boxed{5^2}$.

$c^2 = \boxed{50}$ $\boxed{\textbf{Add}}$ 25 and 25.

$\sqrt{c^2} = \boxed{\sqrt{50}}$ Take the $\boxed{\textbf{square root}}$

of each side.

$c = \boxed{7.1}$ Simplify.

The points are about $\boxed{\textbf{7.1 units}}$ apart.

Your Turn Graph the ordered pairs $(0, -3)$ and $(2, -6)$. Then find the distance between the points.

about 3.6 units

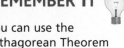

REMEMBER IT

You can use the Pythagorean Theorem to find the distance between two points on a coordinate plane.

EXAMPLE Find Distance on a Map

2 TRAVEL Melissa lives in Chicago. A unit on the grid of her map shown below is 0.08 mile. Find the distance between McCormickville at $(-2, -1)$ and Lake Shore Park at $(2, 2)$.

Let c = the distance between McCormickville and Lake Shore Park. Then a = $\boxed{3}$ and b = $\boxed{4}$.

$c^2 = a^2 + b^2$			Pythagorean Theorem

$c^2 = \boxed{3^2} + \boxed{4^2}$ Replace a with $\boxed{3}$ and b with $\boxed{4}$.

$c^2 = \boxed{9} + \boxed{16}$ Evaluate each power.

$c^2 = \boxed{25}$ Add $\boxed{9}$ and $\boxed{16}$.

$\sqrt{c^2} = \boxed{\sqrt{25}}$ Take the square root of each side.

$c = \boxed{5}$ Simplify.

The distance between McCormickville and Lake Shore Park is $\boxed{5}$ units on the map.

Since each unit equals $\boxed{0.08}$ mile, the distance is

$\boxed{0.08} \times \boxed{5}$ or $\boxed{0.4}$ mile.

Your Turn Refer to Example 2. Find the distance between Shantytown at $(2, -1)$ and the intersection of N. Wabash Ave. and E. Superior St. At $(-1, 1)$.

0.4 mile

© Glencoe/McGraw-Hill

HOMEWORK ASSIGNMENT

Page(s):

Exercises:

BRINGING IT ALL TOGETHER

STUDY GUIDE

FOLDABLES™	**VOCABULARY PUZZLEMAKER**	**BUILD YOUR VOCABULARY**
Use your **Chapter 3 Foldable** to help you study for your chapter test.	To make a crossword puzzle, word search, or jumble puzzle of the vocabulary words in Chapter 3, go to: www.glencoe.com/sec/math/t_resources/free/index.php	You can use your completed **Vocabulary Builder** *(pages 60–61)* to help you solve the puzzle.

3–1
Square Roots

Complete each sentence.

1. The principle square root is the ┃ **positive** ┃ square root of a number.

2. To solve an equation in which one side of the square is a squared term, you can take the ┃ **square root** ┃ of each side of the equation.

Find each square root.

3. $\sqrt{900}$ ┃ **30** ┃

4. $-\sqrt{\dfrac{36}{49}}$ ┃ $-\dfrac{6}{7}$ ┃

5. $-\sqrt{625}$ ┃ **−25** ┃

6. $\sqrt{\dfrac{25}{121}}$ ┃ $\dfrac{5}{11}$ ┃

3–2
Estimating Square Roots

Determine between which two consecutive whole numbers each value is located.

7. $\sqrt{23}$ ┃ **4 and 5** ┃

8. $\sqrt{59}$ ┃ **7 and 8** ┃

9. $\sqrt{27}$ ┃ **5 and 6** ┃

10. $\sqrt{18}$ ┃ **4 and 5** ┃

3–3

The Real Number System

Match the property of real numbers with the algebraic example.

11. Commutative | **b** | **a.** $(x + y) + z = x + (y + z)$

12. Associative | **a** | **b.** $pq = qp$

13. Distributive | **e** | **c.** $h + 0 = h$

14. Identity | **c** | **d.** $c + (-c) = 0$

15. Multiplicative Inverse | **f** | **e.** $x(y + z) = xy + xz$

f. $\dfrac{a}{b} \cdot \dfrac{b}{a} = 1$

3–4

The Pythagorean Theorem

Complete each sentence.

16. If you know the lengths of the two legs of a right triangle, you

    can find the length of the | **hypotenuse** | by finding the

    sum of the squares of their lengths, and then finding the

    | **square root** | of the sum.

17. If you know the lengths of the hypotenuse and one | **leg** |, you

    can find the length of the other leg by subtracting the square of the
    length of the known leg from the square of the length of the

    | **hypotenuse** |, and then finding the square root of the result.

**Use the Pythagorean Theorem to determine whether each
of the following measures of the sides of a triangle are the
sides of a right triangle.**

18. 4, 5, 6 | **no** | 19. 9, 12, 15 | **yes** |

20. 10, 24, 26 | **yes** | 21. 5, 7, 9 | **no** |

3–5

Using the Pythagorean Theorem

22. The triple 8-15-17 is a Pythagorean Triple. Complete the table to find more Pythagorean triples.

	a	b	c	Check: $c^2 = a^2 + b^2$
original	8	15	17	289 = 64 + 225
× 2	16	30	34	1,156 = 256 + 900
× 3	24	45	51	2,601 = 576 + 2,025
× 5	40	75	85	7,225 = 1,600 + 5,625
× 10	80	150	170	28,900 = 6,400 + 22,500

Determine whether each of the following is a Pythagorean triple.

23. 13-84-85   **yes**

24. 11-60-61   **yes**

25. 21-23-29   **no**

26. 12-25-37   **no**

3–6

Distance on the Coordinate Plane

Match each term of the coordinate plane with its description.

27. ordinate   *c*   **a.** one of four sections of the coordinate plane

28. y-axis   *d*   **b.** x-coordinate

29. origin   *f*   **c.** y-coordinate

30. abscissa   *b*   **d.** vertical number line

31. x-axis   *e*   **e.** horizontal number line

                                     f. point where number lines meet

ARE YOU READY FOR THE CHAPTER TEST?

Visit **msmath3.net** to access your textbook, more examples, self-check quizzes, and practice tests to help you study the concepts in Chapter 3.

Check the one that applies. Suggestions to help you study are given with each item.

☐ **I completed the review of all or most lessons without using my notes or asking for help.**

- You are probably ready for the Chapter Test.
- You may want to take the Chapter 3 Practice Test on page 149 of your textbook as a final check.

☐ **I used my Foldable or Study Notebook to complete the review of all or most lessons.**

- You should complete the Chapter 3 Study Guide and Review on pages 146–148 of your textbook.
- If you are unsure of any concepts or skills, refer back to the specific lesson(s).
- You may also want to take the Chapter 3 Practice Test on page 149 of your textbook.

☐ **I asked for help from someone else to complete the review of all or most lessons.**

- You should review the examples and concepts in your Study Notebook and Chapter 3 Foldable.
- Then complete the Chapter 3 Study Guide and Review on pages 146–148 of your textbook.
- If you are unsure of any concepts or skills, refer back to the specific lesson(s).
- You may also want to take the Chapter 3 Practice Test on page 149 of your textbook.

Student Signature	Parent/Guardian Signature

Teacher Signature

Proportions, Algebra, and Geometry

 Use the instructions below to make a Foldable to help you organize your notes as you study the chapter. You will see Foldable reminders in the margin of this Interactive Study Notebook to help you in taking notes.

Begin with a plain sheet of 11" by 17" paper.

STEP 1 **Fold in Thirds**
Fold in thirds widthwise.

STEP 2 **Open and Fold Again**
Fold the bottom to form a pocket. Glue edges.

STEP 3 **Label**
Label each pocket. Place index cards in each pocket.

 NOTE-TAKING TIP: When you take notes, define new vocabulary words, describe new ideas, and write examples that help you remember the meanings of the words and ideas.

BUILD YOUR VOCABULARY

This is an alphabetical list of new vocabulary terms you will learn in Chapter 4. As you complete the study notes for the chapter, you will see Build Your Vocabulary reminders to complete each term's definition or description on these pages. Remember to add the textbook page number in the second column for reference when you study.

Vocabulary Term	Found on Page	Definition	Description or Example
congruent			
corresponding parts			
cross products			
dilation [deye-LAY-shuhn]			
indirect measurement			
polygon			
proportion			
rate			
rate of change			

Vocabulary Term	Found on Page	Definition	Description or Example
ratio			
rise			
run			
scale			
scale drawing			
scale factor			
scale model			
similar			
slope			
unit rate			

BUILD YOUR VOCABULARY (pages 82–83)

© Glencoe/McGraw-Hill

WHAT YOU'LL LEARN

- Express ratios as fractions in simplest form and determine unit rates.

A **ratio** is a comparison of two numbers by division.

A **rate** is a special kind of ratio. It is a comparison of two quantities with different types of units.

When a rate is simplified so it has a denominator of 1, it is called a **unit rate**.

EXAMPLE Write Ratios in Simplest Form

REVIEW IT

What is the greatest common factor of two or more numbers? How can you find it? *(Prerequisite Skill)*

_____

_____

_____

_____

_____

_____

_____

1 Express *12 blue marbles out of 18 marbles* in simplest form.

$$\frac{12}{18} = \frac{2}{3}$$

Divide the numerator and denominator by the greatest common factor, 6.

The ratio of blue marbles to marbles is $\frac{2}{3}$ or 2 out of 3.

EXAMPLE Find a Unit Rate **(parallels Example 3 in text)**

2 READING Yi-Mei reads 141 pages in 3 hours. How many pages does she read per hour?

Write the rate that expresses the comparison of pages to hours. Then find the unit rate.

$$\frac{141 \text{ pages}}{3 \text{ hours}} = \frac{47 \text{ pages}}{1 \text{ hour}}$$

Divide the numerator and denominator by 3 to get a denominator of 1.

Yi-Mei reads an average of 47 pages per hour.

Your Turn Express each ratio in simplest form.

a. 5 blue marbles out of 20 marbles

$$\dfrac{1}{4}$$

b. 14 inches to 2 feet

$$\dfrac{7}{12}$$

c. On a trip from Columbus, Ohio, to Myrtle Beach, South Carolina, Lee drove 864 miles in 14 hours. What was Lee's average speed in miles per hour?

about 62 miles per hour

EXAMPLE Compare Unit Rates **(parallels Example 4 in text)**

3 **SHOPPING** Alex spends $12.50 for 2 pounds of almonds and $23.85 for 5 pounds of jellybeans. Which item costs less per pound? By how much?

For each item, write a rate that compares the cost to the amount. Then find the unit rates.

Almonds: $\dfrac{\$12.50}{2\ \text{pounds}} = \dfrac{\boxed{\$6.25}}{1\ \text{pound}}$

Jellybeans: $\dfrac{\$23.85}{5\ \text{pounds}} = \dfrac{\boxed{\$4.77}}{1\ \text{pound}}$

The almonds cost $\boxed{\$6.25}$ per pound and the jellybeans cost

$\boxed{\$4.77}$ per pound. So, the jellybeans cost $\boxed{\$6.25}$ –

$\boxed{\$4.77}$ or $\boxed{\$1.48}$ per pound less than the almonds.

Your Turn Cameron spends $22.50 for 2 pounds of macadamia nuts and $31.05 for 3 pounds of cashews. Which item costs less per pound? By how much?

cashews by $0.90

FOLDABLES

ORGANIZE IT

Write the definitions of *rate* and *unit rate* on an index card. Then on the other side of the card, write examples of how to find and compare unit rates. Include these cards in your Foldable.

HOMEWORK ASSIGNMENT

Page(s): _____

Exercises: _____

_____

_____

WHAT YOU'LL LEARN

• Find rates of change.

BUILD YOUR VOCABULARY (page 82)

A **rate of change** is a rate that describes how one quantity

| changes | in | relation | to another.

EXAMPLE Find a Rate of Change

1 **DOGS** The table below shows the weight of a dog in pounds between 4 and 12 months old. Find the rate of change in the dog's weight between 8 and 12 months of age.

Age (mo)	4	8	12
Weight (lb)	15	28	43

REMEMBER IT

Rate of change is always expressed as a unit rate.

$$\frac{\text{change in weight}}{\text{change in age}} = \frac{(43 - \boxed{28}) \text{ pounds}}{(\boxed{12} - 8) \text{ months}}$$

The dog grew from 28 to 43 pounds from ages 8 to 12 months.

$$= \frac{\boxed{15} \text{ pounds}}{\boxed{4} \text{ months}}$$

Subtract to find the change in weights and ages.

$$= \frac{\boxed{3.75} \text{ pounds}}{\boxed{1} \text{ month}}$$

Express this rate as a | unit rate .

The dog grew an average of | 3.75 | pounds per | month .

Your Turn The table below shows Julia's height in inches between the ages of 6 and 11. Find the rate of change in her height between ages 6 and 9.

Age (yr)	6	9	11
Height (in.)	52	58	60

2 inches per year

EXAMPLE Find a Negative Rate of Change

KEY CONCEPT

Rate of Change To find the rate of change, divide the difference in the *y*-coordinate by the difference in the *x*-coordinate.

FOLDABLES

Record this concept on one side of an index card. Write an example on the other side of the card.

REMEMBER IT

Always read graphs from left to right.

2 SCHOOLS The graph shows the number of students in the 8th grade between 1998 and 2002. Find the rate of change between 2000 and 2002.

Number of 8th Grade Students

Use the formula for the rate of change.

Let $(x_1, y_1) = (2000, 485)$ and $(x_2, y_2) = (2000, 459)$.

$$\frac{y_2 - y_1}{x_2 - x_1} = \frac{\boxed{459} - \boxed{485}}{\boxed{2002} - \boxed{2000}}$$ Write the formula for the rate of change.

$$= \frac{\boxed{-26}}{\boxed{2}}$$ Simplify.

$$= \frac{\boxed{-13}}{\boxed{1}}$$ Express this as a unit rate.

The rate of change is $\boxed{-13}$ students per $\boxed{\text{year}}$.

Your Turn The graph below shows the number of students in the 6th grade between 1997 and 2003. Find the rate of change between 2001 and 2003.

Number of 6th Grade Students

−24 students per year

EXAMPLES Zero Rates of Change

3 **TEMPERATURE** The graph shows the temperature measured each hour from 10 A.M. to 3 P.M. Find a time period in which the temperature did not change.

Between | **1 P.M.** | and

| **2 P.M.** |, the temperature did

not change. This is shown on the

graph by a | **horizontal** | line.

Temperature Over Time

4 **TEMPERATURE** Refer to Example 3. Find the rate of change from 1 P.M. to 2 P.M.

Let $(x_1, y_1) = (1, 62)$ and $(x_2, y_2) = (2, 62)$.

$$\frac{y_2 - y_1}{x_2 - x_1} = \frac{62 - 62}{2 - 1}$$ Write the formula for the rate of change.

$$= \frac{0}{1} \text{ or } 0$$ Simplify.

The rate of change is | **0°F** | per hour.

Your Turn The graph shows the temperature measured each hour from 10 A.M. to 4 P.M.

a. Find a time period in which the temperature did not change.

| **3 P.M. to 4 P.M.** |

Temperature

b. Find the rate of change from 2 P.M. to 3 P.M.

| **3°F** |

HOMEWORK ASSIGNMENT

Page(s):

Exercises:

Slope

WHAT YOU'LL LEARN

• Find the slope of a line.

BUILD YOUR VOCABULARY (page 83)

Slope is the | ratio | of the **rise**, or | vertical | change,

to the **run**, or | horizontal | change.

EXAMPLE Find Slope Using a Graph

1 Find the slope of the line.

Choose two points on the line. The

vertical change is | −2 | units while

the horizontal change is | 1 | unit.

slope = | rise |
        | ─── |
        | run |

Definition of slope

= | −2 |
  | ─── |
  | 1 |

rise = | −2 |, run = | 1 |

The slope of the line is | −2 |.

REVIEW IT

What is a ratio?
(Lesson 4-1)

_____

_____

_____

_____

Your Turn Find the slope of the line graphed.

$-\dfrac{1}{2}$

EXAMPLE Find Slope Using a Table

2 The points given in the table lie on a line. Find the slope of the line. Then graph the line.

$$-2 \quad\quad -2 \quad\quad -2$$

x	5	3	1	−1
y	−1	0	1	2

$$+1 \quad\quad +1 \quad\quad +1$$

slope $= \dfrac{\text{rise}}{\text{run}}$ ← change in y
← change in x

$= \dfrac{\boxed{1}}{\boxed{-2}}$ or $\boxed{-\dfrac{1}{2}}$

The slope is $\boxed{-\dfrac{1}{2}}$.

Your Turn The points given in the table lie on a line. Find the slope of the line. Then graph the line.

x	−3	0	3	6
y	−1	1	3	5

$\dfrac{2}{3}$

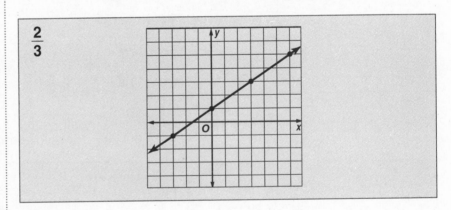

Solving Proportions

WHAT YOU'LL LEARN

- Use proportions to solve problems.

KEY CONCEPTS

Proportion A proportion is an equation stating that two ratios are equivalent.

Property of Proportions The cross products of a proportion are equal.

FOLDABLES

Be sure to include this definition and property in your Foldable.

BUILD YOUR VOCABULARY (page 82)

In a **proportion**, two | ratios | are | equivalent |.

In a proportion, the **cross products** are | equal |.

EXAMPLE Identify a Proportion

1 Determine whether the ratios $\frac{9}{12}$ and $\frac{18}{27}$ form a proportion.

Find the cross products.

$12 \cdot 18 =$ | **216** |

$9 \cdot 27 =$ | **243** |

Since the cross products are not | **equal** |, the ratios do not

form a | **proportion** |.

EXAMPLE Solve a Proportion

2 Solve $\frac{x}{4} = \frac{7}{20}$.

$$\frac{x}{4} = \frac{7}{20}$$ Write the equation.

$x \cdot$ | **20** | $= 4 \cdot$ | **7** | Find the | **cross products** |.

| **20x** | $=$ | **28** | Multiply.

| **20x** / **20** | $=$ | **28** / **20** | Divide each side by 20.

$x =$ | **1.4** | Simplify.

The solution is | **1.4** |.

Your Turn

a. Determine whether the ratios $\frac{7}{21}$ and $\frac{8}{24}$ form a proportion.

> **yes**

b. Solve $\frac{x}{5} = \frac{11}{21}$.

> **2.75**

EXAMPLE Use a Proportion to Solve a Problem

3 **COOKING** A recipe serves 10 people and calls for 3 cups of flour. If you want to make the recipe for 15 people, how many cups of flour should you use?

cups of flour ———▶ $\dfrac{3}{10} = \dfrac{n}{15}$ ◀——— cups of flour
total people served ———▶ $\qquad$ ◀——— total people served

$$\boxed{3 \cdot 15} = \boxed{10 \cdot n} \qquad \text{Find the cross products.}$$

$$45 = 10n \qquad \text{Multiply.}$$

$$\frac{45}{\boxed{10}} = \frac{10n}{\boxed{10}} \qquad \text{Divide each side by } \boxed{10}.$$

$$\boxed{4.5} = n \qquad \text{Simplify.}$$

You will need $\boxed{4.5}$ cups of flour to make the recipe for 15 people.

Your Turn A recipe serves 12 people and calls for 5 cups of sugar. If you want to make the recipe for 18 people, how many cups of sugar should you use?

> **7.5 cups**

HOMEWORK ASSIGNMENT

Page(s):

Exercises:

Similar Polygons

WHAT YOU'LL LEARN

- Identify similar polygons and find missing measures of similar polygons.

KEY CONCEPT

Similar Polygons If two polygons are similar, then

- their corresponding angles are congruent, or have the same measure, and
- their corresponding sides are proportional.

BUILD YOUR VOCABULARY (pages 82–83)

A **polygon** is a simple closed figure in a plane formed

by ⬚ **three or more** line segments.

Polygons that have the ⬚ **same** shape are called **similar** polygons.

The parts of ⬚ **similar** figures that "match" are called **corresponding parts.**

Congruent means to have the ⬚ **same** measure.

EXAMPLE Identify Similar Polygons

① Determine whether triangle *DEF* is similar to triangle *HJK*. Explain your reasoning.

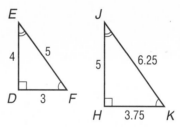

First, check to see if corresponding angles are congruent.

$\angle D \cong \angle H$, $\angle E \cong \angle J$, and $\angle F \cong \angle K$.

Next, check to see if corresponding sides are proportional.

$$\frac{DE}{HJ} = \boxed{\frac{4}{5}} = 0.8 \qquad \frac{EF}{JK} = \boxed{\frac{5}{6.25}} = 0.8$$

$$\frac{DF}{HK} = \boxed{\frac{3}{3.75}} = 0.8$$

Since the corresponding angles are congruent and $\frac{4}{5} = \frac{5}{6.25} = \frac{3}{3.75}$, triangle *DEF* is ⬚ **similar** to triangle *HJK*.

Your Turn Determine whether triangle *ABC* is similar to triangle *TRI*. Explain your reasoning.

> yes; corresponding angles are congruent and $\frac{3}{4.5} = \frac{5}{7.5} = \frac{4}{6}$.

BUILD YOUR VOCABULARY (page 83)

The | **ratio** | of the lengths of two | **corresponding** |

sides of two similar polygons is called the **scale factor**.

EXAMPLE Find Missing Measures

2 **Given that rectangle *GHIJ* ~ rectangle *LMNO*, write a proportion to find the measure of $\overline{NO}$. Then solve.**

The scale factor from rectangle *GHIJ* to rectangle *LMNO* is

$\frac{GJ}{LO}$, which is $\boxed{\dfrac{2}{3}}$. Write a proportion with this scale factor.

Let *n* represent the measure of $\overline{NO}$.

$$\frac{IJ}{NO} = \frac{2}{3}$$

$\overline{IJ}$ corresponds to $\overline{NO}$. The scale factor is $\frac{2}{3}$.

$$\frac{\boxed{4}}{\boxed{n}} = \frac{2}{3}$$

$IJ = \boxed{4}$ and $NO = \boxed{n}$

$\boxed{4} \cdot 3 = \boxed{n} \cdot 2$ Find the cross products.

$\boxed{12} = \boxed{2n}$ Multiply.

$\boxed{6} = \boxed{n}$ Divide each side by 2. Simplify.

The measure of $\overline{NO}$ is $\boxed{6}$.

Your Turn

Given that rectangle *ABCD* ~ rectangle *WXYZ*, write a proportion to find the measure of $\overline{ZY}$. Then solve.

$$\frac{3}{6} = \frac{7.5}{n}; 15$$

HOMEWORK ASSIGNMENT

Page(s):

Exercises:

4–6 **Scale Drawings and Models**

WHAT YOU'LL LEARN

• Solve problems involving scale drawings.

BUILD YOUR VOCABULARY (page 83)

A **scale drawing** or a **scale model** is used to represent an object that is too [large] or too [small] to be drawn or built at actual size.

The **scale** is determined by the [ratio] of given length on a [drawing or model] to the corresponding actual length of the object.

EXAMPLE Find a Missing Measurement

1 **MAPS** The distance from Bingston to Alanton is 1.5 inches on the map. Find the actual distance.

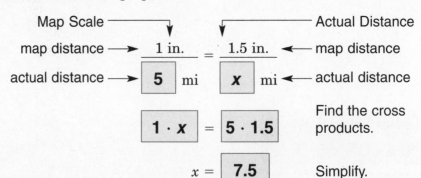

Scale: 1 in. = 5 mi

Let x represent the actual distance from Bingston to Alanton. Write and solve a proportion.

Map Scale — Actual Distance

map distance → $\dfrac{1 \text{ in.}}{\boxed{5} \text{ mi}} = \dfrac{1.5 \text{ in.}}{\boxed{x} \text{ mi}}$ ← map distance
actual distance ← actual distance

$\boxed{1 \cdot x} = \boxed{5 \cdot 1.5}$ Find the cross products.

$x = \boxed{7.5}$ Simplify.

The actual distance from Bingston to Alanton is

7.5 miles .

REMEMBER IT

Scales and scale factors are usually written so that the drawing length comes first in the ratio.

EXAMPLE Find the Scale Factor

2 MAPS Refer to Example 1. Find the scale factor for the map.

$$\frac{1 \text{ in.}}{5 \text{ mi}} = \frac{1 \text{ in.}}{316,800 \text{ in.}}$$ Convert 5 miles to inches.

The scale factor is $\boxed{\dfrac{1}{316,800}}$ or $\boxed{1:316,800}$.

Your Turn The distance from Springfield to Capital City is 1.4 inches on the map.

a. Find the actual distance.

$\boxed{\textbf{9.8 miles}}$

b. Find the scale factor for the map.

$\boxed{\dfrac{1}{443,520} \text{ or } 1:443,520}$

EXAMPLE Find the Scale

3 SCALE DRAWINGS A wall in a room is 15 feet long. On a scale drawing it is shown as 6 inches. What is the scale of the drawing?

Write and solve a proportion to find the scale of the drawing.

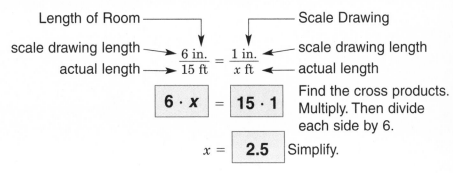

So, the scale is 1 inch = $\boxed{\textbf{2.5 feet}}$.

Your Turn The length of a garage is 24 feet. On a scale drawing the length of the garage is 10 inches. What is the scale of the drawing?

$\boxed{\textbf{1 inch = 2.4 feet}}$

FOLDABLES

ORGANIZE IT

Write definitions of *scale, scale drawing,* and *scale model* on cards and give your own examples. Be sure to explain how to create a scale for a scale drawing or model.

HOMEWORK ASSIGNMENT

Page(s):

Exercises:

WHAT YOU'LL LEARN

• Solve problems involving similar triangles.

BUILD YOUR VOCABULARY (page 82)

Indirect measurement uses the properties of similar polygons and **proportions** to measure distance of lengths that are too **difficult** to measure directly.

EXAMPLE Use Shadow Reckoning

1 **TREES** A tree in front of Marcel's house has a shadow 12 feet long. At the same time, Marcel has a shadow 3 feet long. If Marcel is 5.5 feet tall, how tall is the tree?

h ft

5.5 ft

3 ft

12 ft

WRITE IT

Which property of similar polygons is used to set up the proportion for the shadow and height of Marcel and the tree?

_____

_____

_____

_____

tree's shadow $\longrightarrow$ $\dfrac{12}{3} = \dfrac{h}{5.5}$ $\longleftarrow$ tree's height
Marcel's shadow $\longrightarrow$ $\longleftarrow$ Marcel's height

| $12 \cdot 5.5$ = $3 \cdot h$ | Find the cross products. |

| 66 = 3h | Multiply. |

| $\dfrac{66}{3} = \dfrac{3h}{3}$ | Divide each side by **3**. |

| 22 = h | Simplify. |

The tree is **22** feet tall.

Your Turn Jayson casts a shadow that is 10 feet. At the same time, a flagpole casts a shadow that is 40 feet. If the flagpole is 20 feet tall, how tall is Jayson?

5 feet

EXAMPLE Use Indirect Measurement

2 **SURVEYING** The two triangles shown in the figure are similar. Find the distance *d* across the stream.

In this figure $\triangle ABC \sim \triangle EDC$.

So, $\overline{AB}$ corresponds to $\overline{ED}$, and $\overline{BC}$ corresponds to **DC**.

$$\frac{AB}{ED} = \frac{BC}{DC}$$ Write a **proportion** .

$$\boxed{\frac{48}{d}} = \boxed{\frac{60}{20}}$$ $AB = 48$, $ED = d$, $BC = 60$, and $DC = 20$

$$\boxed{48 \cdot 20} = \boxed{d \cdot 60}$$ Find the cross products.

$$\boxed{\frac{960}{60}} = \boxed{\frac{60d}{60}}$$ Multiply. Then divide each side by $\boxed{60}$.

$$\boxed{16} = d$$ Simplify.

The distance across the stream is **16 meters** .

FOLDABLES

ORGANIZE IT

Include a definition of *indirect measurement.* Also include an explanation of how to use indirect measurement with your own words or sketch.

Your Turn The two triangles shown in the figure are similar. Find the distance d across the river.

7 feet

© Glencoe/McGraw-Hill

WHAT YOU'LL LEARN

• Graph dilations on a coordinate plane.

BUILD YOUR VOCABULARY (page 82)

The image produced by enlarging or reducing a figure is called a **dilation**.

EXAMPLE Graph a Dilation

① Graph △*MNO* with vertices *M*(3, −1), *N*(2, −2), and *O*(0, 4). Then graph its image △*M′N′O′* after a dilation with a scale factor of $\frac{3}{2}$.

To find the vertices of the dilation, multiply each coordinate in the ordered pairs by $\frac{3}{2}$. Then graph both images on the same axes.

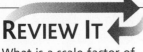

REVIEW IT

What is a scale factor of similar polygons? *(Lesson 4-5)*

_____

_____

_____

_____

_____

$M(3, -1) \longrightarrow \left(3 \cdot \frac{3}{2}, -1 \cdot \frac{3}{2}\right) \longrightarrow M'\left(\frac{9}{2}, -\frac{3}{2}\right)$

$N(2, -2) \longrightarrow \left(2 \cdot \frac{3}{2}, -2 \cdot \frac{3}{2}\right) \longrightarrow N'\ (3, -3)$

$O(0, 4) \longrightarrow \left(0 \cdot \frac{3}{2}, 4 \cdot \frac{3}{2}\right) \longrightarrow O'\ (0, 6)$

CHECK Draw lines through the origin and each of the vertices of the original figure. The vertices of the dilation should lie on those same lines.

Your Turn Graph $\triangle JKL$ with vertices $J(2, 4)$, $K(4, -6)$, and $L(0, -4)$. Then graph its image $\triangle J'K'L'$ after a dilation with a scale factor of $\frac{1}{2}$.

EXAMPLE Find and Classify a Scale Factor

REMEMBER IT 💡

- If the scale factor is between 0 and 1, the dilation is a reduction.
- If the scale factor is greater than 1, the dilation is an enlargement.
- If the scale factor is equal to 1, the dilation is the same size as the original figure.

❷ In the figure, segment $X'Y'$ is a dilation of segment XY. Find the scale factor of the dilation, and classify it as an enlargement or as a reduction.

Write a ratio of the x- or y-coordinate of one vertex of the dilation to the x- or y-coordinate of the corresponding vertex of the original figure. Use the y-coordinates of $X(-4, 2)$ and $X'(-2, 1)$.

$$\frac{y\text{-coordinate of } X'}{y\text{-coordinate of } X} = \boxed{\frac{1}{2}}$$

The scale factor is $\boxed{\dfrac{1}{2}}$. Since the image is smaller than the

original figure, the dilation is a $\boxed{\textbf{reduction}}$.

Your Turn In the figure, segment $A'B'$ is a dilation of segment AB. Find the scale factor of the dilation, and classify it as an *enlargement* or as a *reduction*.

2; enlargement

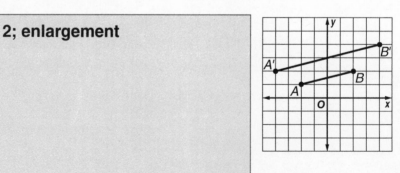

HOMEWORK ASSIGNMENT

Page(s):

Exercises:

BRINGING IT ALL TOGETHER

STUDY GUIDE

FOLDABLES™	**VOCABULARY PUZZLEMAKER**	**BUILD YOUR VOCABULARY**
Use your **Chapter 4 Foldable** to help you study for your chapter test.	To make a crossword puzzle, word search, or jumble puzzle of the vocabulary words in Chapter 4, go to: www.glencoe.com/sec/math/t_resources/free/index.php	You can use your completed **Vocabulary Builder** (*pages 82–83*) to help you solve the puzzle.

4-1
Ratios and Rates

Match each phrase with the term they describe.

1. a comparison of two numbers **c**

2. a comparison of two quantities with different types of units **d**

3. a rate that is simplified so it has a denominator of 1 **a**

a. unit rate
b. numerator
c. ratio
d. rate

4. Express 12 wins to 14 losses in simplest form. $\dfrac{6}{7}$, **6:7, or 6 to 7**

5. Express 6 inches of rain in 4 hours as a unit rate. **1.5 in/h**

4-2
Rate of Change

Use the table shown to answer each question.

Week	Bicycles Sold
2	2
4	14
6	14
8	12

6. Find the rate of change in the number of bicycles sold between weeks 2 and 4.

   12 bicycles per 2 weeks

7. Between which weeks is the rate of change negative? **6 and 8**

4-3
Slope

8. Complete the statement.

Slope is the ratio of the vertical [change] between two

points to the [horizontal] change between the points.

9. The points given in the table lie on
a line. Find the slope of the line.

x	-4	-2	2	4
y	2	1	-1	-2

[-2]

4-4
Solving Proportions

10. Do the ratios $\frac{a}{b}$ and $\frac{c}{d}$ always form a proportion? Why or why not?

[**No; Sample answer: The ratios only form a proportion if the cross products *ad* and *bc* are equal.**]

Solve each proportion.

11. $\frac{7}{b} = \frac{35}{5}$

[**1**]

12. $\frac{a}{16} = \frac{3}{8}$

[**6**]

13. $\frac{4}{13} = \frac{3}{c}$

[**4.75**]

4-5
Similar Polygons

14. If two polygons have corresponding angles that are congruent, does that mean that the polygons are similar? Why or why not?

[**Sample answer: No; the polygons are similar only if their corresponding sides are proportional as well.**]

15. Rectangle *ABCD* has side lengths of 30 and 5. Rectangle *EFGH* has side lengths of 15 and 3. Determine whether the rectangles are similar.

[**The rectangles are not similar.**]

4-6
Scale Drawings and Models

16. The scale on a map is 1 inch = 20 miles.

    Find the actual distance for the map distance of $\frac{5}{8}$ inch.

12.5 mi

17. What is the scale factor for a model if part of the model that is 4 inches corresponds to a real-life object that is 16 inches.

$\dfrac{1}{4}$

4-7
Indirect Measurement

18. Complete the following sentence.

    When you solve a problem using shadow reckoning, the objects being compared and their shadows form two sides

    of | **similar** | triangles.

19. **STATUE** If a statue casts a 6-foot shadow and a 5-foot mailbox casts a 4-foot shadow, how tall is the statue?

7.5 ft

4-8
Dilations

20. If you are given the coordinates of a figure and the scale factor of a dilation of that figure, how can you find the coordinates of the new figure?

Sample answer: Multiply each coordinate by the scale factor.

21. Complete the table.

If the scale factor is	Then the dilation is
between 0 and 1	**a reduction**
greater than 1	**an enlargement**
equal to 1	**the same size as the horizontal figure**

ARE YOU READY FOR THE CHAPTER TEST?

Visit **msmath3.net** to access your textbook, more examples, self-check quizzes, and practice tests to help you study the concepts in Chapter 4.

Check the one that applies. Suggestions to help you study are given with each item.

☐ **I completed the review of all or most lessons without using my notes or asking for help.**

- You are probably ready for the Chapter Test.

- You may want to take the Chapter 4 Practice Test on page 201 of your textbook as a final check.

☐ **I used my Foldable or Study Notebook to complete the review of all or most lessons.**

- You should complete the Chapter 4 Study Guide and Review on pages 198–200 of your textbook.

- If you are unsure of any concepts or skills, refer to the specific lesson(s).

- You may also want to take the Chapter 4 Practice Test on page 201.

☐ **I asked for help from someone else to complete the review of all or most lessons.**

- You should review the examples and concepts in your Study Notebook and Chapter 4 Foldable.

- Then complete the Chapter 4 Study Guide and Review on pages 198–200 of your textbook.

- If you are unsure of any concepts or skills, refer to the specific lesson(s).

- You may also want to take the Chapter 4 Practice Test on page 201.

Student Signature

Parent/Guardian Signature

Teacher Signature

Use the instructions below to make a Foldable to help you organize your notes as you study the chapter. You will see Foldable reminders in the margin of this Interactive Study Notebook to help you in taking notes.

Begin with 4 sheets of $8\frac{1}{2}$" × 11" paper.

STEP 1 **Draw a Circle**
Draw a large circle on one of the sheets of paper.

STEP 2 **Stack and Cut**
Stack the sheets of paper. Place the one with the circle on top. Cut all four sheets in the shape of a circle.

STEP 3 **Staple and Label**
Staple the circles on the left side. Write the first four lesson numbers on each circle.

Lesson 5-1

STEP 4 **Turn and Label**
Turn the circles to the back side so that the staples are still on the left. Write the last four lesson numbers one each circle.

Lesson 5-5

 NOTE-TAKING TIP: When you take notes, it may help to create a visual representation, such as a drawing or a chart, to organize the information you learn. When you use a visual, be sure to clearly label it.

BUILD YOUR VOCABULARY

This is an alphabetical list of new vocabulary terms you will learn in Chapter 5. As you complete the study notes for the chapter, you will see Build Your Vocabulary reminders to complete each term's definition or description on these pages. Remember to add the textbook page number in the second column for reference when you study.

Vocabulary Term	Found on Page	Definition	Description or Example
base			
compatible numbers			
discount			
interest			
markup			
part			
percent			

© Glencoe/McGraw-Hill

Vocabulary Term	Found on Page	Definition	Description or Example
percent equation			
percent of change			
percent of decrease			
percent of increase			
percent proportion			
principle			
selling price			

Ratios and Percents

WHAT YOU'LL LEARN

• Write ratios as percents and vice versa.

KEY CONCEPT

Percent A percent is a ratio that compares a number to 100.

BUILD YOUR VOCABULARY (page 108)

| **Ratios** | such as 27 out of 100 or 8 out of 25 |

can be written as **percents**.

EXAMPLES Write Ratios as Percents

1 **POPULATION** According to the 2000 U.S. Census Bureau, 13 out of every 100 people living in Delaware were 65 or older. Write this ratio as a percent.

13 out of every **100** = 13%

2 **BASEBALL** In 2001, Manny Ramirez got on base 40.5 times for every 100 times he was at bat. Write this ratio as a percent.

40.5 out of **100** = 40.5%

Your Turn Write each ratio as a percent.

a. 59 out of 100

59%

b. 68 out of 100

68%

EXAMPLES Write Ratios and Fractions as Percents

3 **TRANSPORTATION** About 4 out of 5 commuters in the United States drive or carpool to work. Write this ratio as a percent.

$$\frac{4}{5} = \frac{80}{100}$$

× **20**

× **20**

$$\frac{4}{5} = \frac{80}{100}$$

So, **4** out of **5** equals **80%** .

FOLDABLES

ORGANIZE IT

Write in words and symbols what you've learned about expressing ratios as percents.

Lesson 5-1

4 INTERNET In 2000, about $\frac{3}{200}$ of the population in Peru used the Internet. Write this fraction as a percent.

$\div$ **2**

$$\frac{3}{200} = \frac{1.5}{100}$$

$\div$ **2**

$\frac{3}{200}$ = $\frac{1.5}{100}$

So, **3** out of **200** equals **1.5%** .

Your Turn Write each ratio or fraction as a percent.

a. 3 out of 5

b. $\frac{122}{200}$ of teens

60%

61%

EXAMPLE Write Percents as Fractions

5 SCHEDULE The circle graph shows an estimate of the percent of his day that Peter spends on each activity. Write the percents for eating and sleeping as fractions in simplest form.

Eating: 5% = $\frac{5}{100}$ or $\frac{1}{20}$

Sleeping: 35% = $\frac{35}{100}$ or $\frac{7}{120}$

How Peter Spends His Day

15% Other
35% Sleep
15% Television
5% Eat
30% School

HOMEWORK ASSIGNMENT

Page(s): _____

Exercises: _____

Your Turn The circle graph shows an estimate of the percent of his day that Leon spends on each activity. Write the percents for school and television as fractions in simplest form.

school: $\frac{1}{5}$; television: $\frac{3}{20}$

How Leon Spends His Day

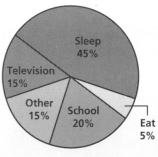

Sleep 45%
Television 15%
Other 15%
School 20%
Eat 5%

Fractions, Decimals, and Percents

EXAMPLES Percents as Decimals

WHAT YOU'LL LEARN

- Write percents as fractions and decimals and vice versa.

Write each percent as a decimal.

1 52%

$$52\% = 52\%$$

Divide by **100** and remove the percent symbol.

$$= 0.52$$

KEY CONCEPTS

Decimals and Percents

To write a percent as a decimal, divide by 100 and remove the percent symbol.

To write a decimal as a percent, multiply by 100 and add the percent symbol.

2 245%

$$245\% = 245\%$$

Divide by **100** and remove the percent symbol.

$$= 2.45$$

Your Turn Write each percent as a decimal.

a. 28%

0.28

b. 135%

1.35

EXAMPLES Decimals as Percents

Write each decimal as a percent.

3 0.3

$$0.3 = 0.30$$

Multiply by **100** and add the percent symbol.

$$= 30\%$$

4 0.71

$$0.71 = 0.71$$

Multiply by **100** and add the percent symbol.

$$= 71\%$$

Your Turn Write each decimal as a percent.

a. 0.91

91%

b. 1.65

165%

EXAMPLES Fractions as Percents

5 Write $\frac{3}{4}$ as a percent.

Method 1

Use a proportion.

$$\frac{3}{4} = \frac{x}{100}$$

$$3 \cdot 100 = \boxed{4 \cdot x}$$

$$300 = \boxed{4x}$$

$$\boxed{\frac{300}{4}} = \boxed{\frac{4x}{4}}$$

$$\boxed{75} = x$$

So, $\frac{3}{4}$ can be written as $\boxed{75\%}$.

Method 2

Write as a decimal.

$$\frac{3}{4} = 0.75$$

$$= \boxed{75\%}$$

$$\begin{array}{r} 0.75 \\ 4)\overline{3.00} \\ \underline{28} \\ 20 \\ \underline{20} \\ 0 \end{array}$$

6 Write $\frac{1}{6}$ as a percent.

Method 1

Use a proportion.

$$\frac{1}{6} = \frac{x}{100}$$

$$\boxed{1 \cdot 100} = 6 \cdot x$$

$$\boxed{100} = 6x$$

$$\boxed{\frac{100}{6}} = \boxed{\frac{6x}{6}}$$

$$\boxed{16.\overline{6}} = x$$

So, $\frac{1}{6}$ can be written as $\boxed{16.\overline{6}\%}$.

Method 2

Write as a decimal.

$$\frac{1}{6} = 0.16\overline{6}$$

$$= \boxed{16.\overline{6}\%}$$

$$\begin{array}{r} 0.116... \\ 6)\overline{1.0000} \\ \underline{6} \\ 40 \\ \underline{36} \\ 40 \\ \underline{36} \\ 4 \end{array}$$

REVIEW IT

Show an example of how to write fractions as decimals. *(Lesson 2–1)*

_____

_____

_____

_____

_____

_____

ORGANIZE IT

Write in words and symbols what you have learned about the relationship between percents, decimals, and fractions.

Lesson
5-2

Your Turn Write each fraction as a percent.

a. $\frac{1}{4}$

b. $\frac{1}{9}$

25%

11.$\overline{1}$%

EXAMPLE Compare Numbers

7 **POLITICS** In Sun City, $\frac{9}{20}$ of voters are Democrats. In Moon Town, 48% of voters are Democrats. In which town is there a greater proportion of Democrats?

Write $\frac{9}{20}$ as a percent.

$$\frac{9}{20} = 0.45 \qquad 9 \div 20 = 0.45$$

$= \boxed{45\%}$ $\boxed{\textbf{Multiply by 100}}$ and

add the $\boxed{\textbf{percent}}$ symbol.

Since $\boxed{45\%}$ is less than $\boxed{48\%}$, there are $\boxed{\textbf{more}}$

Democrats in Moon Town.

Your Turn In Star City, $\frac{3}{20}$ of voters are Republicans. In Meteorville, 13% of voters are Republicans. In which town is there a greater proportion of Republicans?

Star City

HOMEWORK ASSIGNMENT

Page(s):

Exercises:

5-3 **The Percent Proportion**

WHAT YOU'LL LEARN

• Solve problems using the percent proportion.

KEY CONCEPT

Percent Proportion

$\dfrac{\text{part}}{\text{base}} = \dfrac{\text{percent}}{100}$

BUILD YOUR VOCABULARY (pages 108–109)

In a **percent proportion**, one one of the numbers, called the **part**, is being compared to the whole quantity, called the **base**. The other ratio is the percent, written as a fraction, whose base is 100 .

EXAMPLE Find the Percent

1 **34 is what percent of 136?**

Since 34 is being compared to 136, 34 is part and 136 is the base. You need to find the percent.

$$\frac{a}{b} = \frac{p}{100} \rightarrow \frac{34}{136} = \frac{p}{100} \qquad a = 34, b = 136$$

34 · 100 = 136 · p   Find the cross products.

3,400 = 136p   Multiply.

$\dfrac{3,400}{136} = \dfrac{136p}{136}$ Divide each side by 136.

25 = p   Simplify.

So, 34 is 25% of 136.

Your Turn 63 is what percent of 210?

30%

© Glencoe/McGraw-Hill

ORGANIZE IT

Be sure to explain how to find the percent, the part, and the base of a percent proportion. You also may want to show the ideas in a chart like the Concept Summary in your text.

Lesson 5-3

EXAMPLE Find the Part

2 **What number is 70% of 600?**

The percent is 70, and the base is 600. You need to find the part.

$$\frac{a}{b} = \frac{p}{100} \rightarrow \frac{a}{600} = \frac{70}{100}$$ $b = 600, p = 70$

$a \cdot 100 = 600 \cdot 70$ Find the cross products.

$100a = \boxed{42{,}000}$ Multiply.

$$\frac{100a}{\boxed{100}} = \frac{42{,}000}{\boxed{100}}$$ Divide each side by $\boxed{100}$.

$a = \boxed{420}$ Simplify.

So, $\boxed{420}$ is 70% of 600.

Your Turn What number is 40% of 400?

$\boxed{160}$

EXAMPLE Find the Base

3 **BASEBALL From 1999 to 2001, Derek Jeter had 11 hits with bases loaded. This was about 30% of his at bats with bases loaded. How many times was he at bat with bases loaded?**

The percent is 30 and the part is 11. Find the base.

$$\frac{a}{b} = \frac{p}{100} \rightarrow \frac{11}{b} = \frac{30}{100}$$ $a = 11, p = 30$

$11 \cdot 100 = b \cdot 30$ Find the cross products.

$\boxed{1{,}100} = \boxed{30b}$ Multiply.

$$\frac{1{,}100}{\boxed{30}} = \frac{30b}{\boxed{30}}$$ Divide each side by $\boxed{30}$.

$\boxed{36.7} \approx b$ Simplify.

Derek Jeter was at bat about $\boxed{37}$ times with bases loaded.

Your Turn In the 2002 season, Barry Bonds had 149 hits. This was about 37% of his at bats. How many times was he at bat?

$\boxed{403}$

HOMEWORK ASSIGNMENT

Page(s):

Exercises:

© Glencoe/McGraw-Hill

Finding Percents Mentally

Use Fractions to Compute Mentally

What You'll Learn

• Compute mentally with percents.

Compute mentally.

1 **40% of 80**

$$40\% \text{ of } 80 = \boxed{\frac{2}{5}} \text{ of } 80 \text{ or } \boxed{32}$$ Use the fraction form of 40%, which is $\boxed{\frac{2}{5}}$.

2 $66\frac{2}{3}\%$ **of 75**

$$66\frac{2}{3}\% \text{ of } 75 = \boxed{\frac{2}{3}} \text{ of } 75 \text{ or } \boxed{50}.$$ Use the fraction form of $66\frac{2}{3}\%$, which is $\boxed{\frac{2}{3}}$.

EXAMPLES Use Decimals to Compute Mentally

Compute mentally.

3 **10% of 65**

$$10\% \text{ of } 65 = \boxed{0.1} \text{ of } 65 \text{ or } \boxed{6.5}$$

4 **1% of 304**

$$1\% \text{ of } 304 = \boxed{0.01} \text{ of } 304 \text{ or } \boxed{3.04}$$

Write It

Explain how you can move the decimal point to mentally multiply 0.1 by 1.1.

_____

_____

_____

_____

Your Turn Compute mentally.

a. 20% of 60

$$\boxed{12}$$

b. $66\frac{2}{3}\%$ of 300

$$\boxed{200}$$

c. 10% of 13

$$\boxed{1.3}$$

d. 1% of 244

$$\boxed{2.44}$$

EXAMPLE Use Mental Math to Solve a Problem

5 TECHNOLOGY A company produces 2,500 of a particular printer. They later discover that 25% of the printers have defects. How many printers from this group have defects?

Method 1 Use a fraction.

25% of 2,500 = $\boxed{\dfrac{1}{4}}$ of 2,500

THINK $\dfrac{1}{4}$ of 2,000 is $\boxed{500}$ and $\dfrac{1}{4}$ of 500 is $\boxed{125}$.

So, $\boxed{\dfrac{1}{4}}$ of 2,500 is $\boxed{500}$ + $\boxed{125}$ or $\boxed{625}$.

Method 2 Use a decimal.

25% of 2,500 = $\boxed{0.25}$ of 2,500

THINK 0.5 of 2,500 is $\boxed{1,250}$.

So, 0.25 of 2,500 is $\boxed{\dfrac{1}{2}}$ · $\boxed{1250}$ or $\boxed{625}$.

There were $\boxed{625}$ printers that had defects.

Your Turn A company produces 1,400 of a particular monitor. They later discover that 20% of the monitors have defects. How many monitors from this group have defects?

280

© Glencoe/McGraw-Hill

FOLDABLES

ORGANIZE IT

In your Foldable, be sure to include examples that show how to estimate percents of numbers.

Lesson
5-4

HOMEWORK ASSIGNMENT

Page(s):

Exercises:

Percent and Estimation

WHAT YOU'LL LEARN

• Estimate by using equivalent fractions, decimals, and percents.

BUILD YOUR VOCABULARY (page 108)

Compatible numbers are two numbers that are easy to add, subtract, multiply, or divide mentally.

EXAMPLES Estimate Percents of Numbers

Estimate.

1 **48% of 70**

48% is about $\boxed{50\%}$ or $\boxed{\dfrac{1}{2}}$. $\boxed{\dfrac{1}{2}}$ and 70 are

compatible numbers.

$\boxed{\dfrac{1}{2}}$ of 70 is $\boxed{35}$.

So, 48% of 70 is about $\boxed{35}$.

2 **75% of 98**

75% is $\dfrac{3}{4}$, and 98 is about $\boxed{100}$. $\dfrac{3}{4}$ and $\boxed{100}$ are

compatible numbers.

$\dfrac{3}{4}$ of $\boxed{100}$ is $\boxed{75}$.

So, 75% of 98 is about $\boxed{75}$.

3 **12% of 81**

12% is about 12.5% or $\boxed{\dfrac{1}{8}}$, $\boxed{\dfrac{1}{8}}$ and $\boxed{80}$ are

and 81 is about $\boxed{80}$.   compatible numbers.

$\boxed{\dfrac{1}{8}}$ of $\boxed{80}$ is $\boxed{10}$.

So, 12% of 81 is about $\boxed{10}$.

Your Turn Estimate.

a. 51% of 60

30

b. 25% of 33

8

c. 37% of 17

8

EXAMPLES Estimate Percents

Estimate each percent.

4 12 out of 47

$\frac{12}{47} \approx \boxed{\frac{12}{48}}$ or $\frac{1}{4}$

47 is about $\boxed{48}$.

$\frac{1}{4} = \boxed{25}$ %

So, 12 out of 47 is about $\boxed{25\%}$.

5 19 out of 31

$\frac{19}{31} \approx \boxed{\frac{20}{30}}$ or $\frac{2}{3}$

19 is about $\boxed{20}$, and

31 is about $\boxed{30}$.

$\frac{2}{3} = \boxed{66\frac{2}{3}}$ %

So, 19 out of 31 is about $\boxed{66\frac{2}{3}\%}$.

6 41 out of 200

$\frac{41}{200} \approx \boxed{\frac{40}{200}}$ or $\frac{1}{5}$

41 is about $\boxed{40}$.

$\frac{1}{5} = \boxed{20\%}$

So, 41 out of 200 is about $\boxed{20\%}$.

FOLDABLES

ORGANIZE IT

Include the meaning of the symbol "≈." You may wish to include an example of estimating a percent in which the symbol ≈ is used.

Lesson 5-5

Your Turn Estimate each percent.

a. 15 out of 76

b. 14 out of 47

c. 11 out of 100

20%

$33\frac{1}{3}$%

10%

EXAMPLE Estimate Percent of an Area

7 ART An artist creates a design on a grid. Estimate the percent of the grid that has been painted so far.

About 6 squares out of 20 squares are covered with paint.

$$\frac{6}{20} = \frac{3}{10} \longrightarrow \frac{3}{10} = \boxed{30\%}$$

So, about **30%** of the grid has been painted.

Your Turn An artist created a design on a grid. Estimate the percent of the grid has been painted so far.

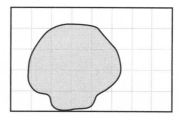

about 35%

HOMEWORK ASSIGNMENT

Page(s):

Exercises:

5–6 The Percent Equation

WHAT YOU'LL LEARN

- Solve problems using the percent equation.

BUILD YOUR VOCABULARY (page 109)

The **percent equation** is an equivalent form of the percent proportion in which the [**percent**] is written as a

[**decimal**] .

EXAMPLE Find the Part

① Find 30% of 450.

The percent is [**30**] %, and the base is [**450**] .

Let *n* represent the part.

$n = $ [**0.30**] · [**450**]   Write 30% as the decimal [**0.30**] .

$n = $ [**135**]   Simplify.

So, 30% of 450 is [**135**] .

REVIEW IT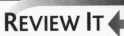

Explain how to write a decimal as a percent. *(Lesson 5-2)*

_____

_____

_____

_____

_____

_____

EXAMPLE Find the Percent

② 102 is what percent of 150?

The part is [**102**] , and the base is [**150**] .

Let *n* represent the percent.

[**102**] $= n \cdot$ [**150**]   Write the equation.

$\dfrac{102}{150} = \dfrac{150n}{150}$ Divide each side by 150.

[**0.68**] $= n$ Simplify.

In the percent equation, the percent is written as a

[**decimal**] . Since [**0.68**] $= 68\%$, 102 is 68% of 150.

122   *Mathematics: Applications and Concepts, Course 3*

© Glencoe/McGraw-Hill

ORGANIZE IT

Write the percent equation in words and symbols. Explain why the rate in a percent equation is usually written as a decimal.

Lesson
5-6

EXAMPLE Find the Base

3 **144 is 45% of what number?**

The part is **144** , and the percent is **45** %.

Let n represent the **base** .

$$144 = \boxed{0.45}\, n$$ Write 45% as a decimal.

$$\frac{144}{\boxed{0.45}} = \frac{\boxed{0.45}\, n}{\boxed{0.45}}$$ Divide each side by 0.45.

$$\boxed{320} = n$$ Simplify.

Your Turn Find the part, percent, or base.

a. Find 20% of 315.

63

b. 135 is what percent of 250?

54%

c. 186 is 30% of what number?

620

EXAMPLE Solve a Real-Life Problem

4 **SALES TAX** The price of a sweater is $75. The sales tax is $5\frac{3}{4}$ percent. What is the total price of the sweater?

You need to find what amount is $5\frac{3}{4}$% of $75.

Let t = the amount of tax.

$$t = \boxed{0.0575} \cdot \boxed{75}$$ Write the equation.

$$t = \boxed{4.3125}$$ Simplify.

The amount of tax is **$4.31** . The total cost of the sweater

is $75 + **$4.31** or **$79.31** .

HOMEWORK ASSIGNMENT

Page(s):

Exercises:

Your Turn The price of a pair of tennis shoes is $60. The sales tax is 5 percent. What is the total price of the shoes?

$63

Percent of Change

WHAT YOU'LL LEARN

• Find and use the percent of increase or decrease.

BUILD YOUR VOCABULARY (page 109)

A **percent of change** is a $\boxed{\text{ratio}}$ that compares the change in quantity to the original amount. When the new amount is $\boxed{\text{greater}}$ than the original, the percent of change is called a **percent of increase**.

When the new amount is $\boxed{\text{less}}$ than the original, the percent of change is called a **percent of decrease**.

EXAMPLE Find the Percent of Increase

KEY CONCEPT

Percent of Change A percent of change is a ratio that compares the change in quantity to the original amount.

① **HOMES** The Nietos bought a house several years ago for $120,000. This year, they sold it for $150,000. Find the percent of increase.

Step 1 Subtract to find the amount of change.

$$150{,}000 - 120{,}000 = \boxed{30{,}000}$$

Step 2 Write a ratio that compares the amount of $\boxed{\text{change}}$ to the $\boxed{\text{original}}$ amount they paid for the house. Express the ratio as a percent.

Percent of change $= \dfrac{\text{amount of change}}{\text{original amount}}$ Definition of percent of change

$$= \dfrac{\boxed{30{,}000}}{\boxed{120{,}000}}$$

$$= 0.25 \text{ or } \boxed{25}\%$$

The percent of increase is $\boxed{25}$ %.

Your Turn Last year Cedar Park Swim Club had 340 members. This year they have 391 members. Find the percent increase.

15%

FOLDABLES

ORGANIZE IT

Be sure to include an explanation and examples showing the difference between percent of increase and percent of decrease.

Lesson
5-7

2 **SCHOOLS** Johnson Middle School had 240 students last year. This year, there are 192 students. Find the percent of change. State whether the percent of change is an increase or a decrease.

Step 1 Subtract to find the amount of change.

$$240 - 192 = \boxed{48}$$

Step 2 Write a ratio that compares the amount of change to the number of students last year. Express the ratio as a percent.

$$\text{Percent of change} = \frac{\text{amount of change}}{\text{original amount}}$$

$$= \frac{\boxed{48}}{\boxed{240}}$$

$$= 0.20 \text{ or } \boxed{20\%}$$

The percent of change is $\boxed{20\%}$. Since the new amount is $\boxed{\text{less}}$ than the original, it is a percent of $\boxed{\text{decrease}}$.

Your Turn Meagan bought a new car several years ago for $14,000. This year she sold the car for $9,100. Find the percent of change. State whether the percent of change is an *increase* or a *decrease*.

35%; decrease

BUILD YOUR VOCABULARY (pages 108–109)

The **markup** is the amount the price of an item is

$\boxed{\text{increased}}$ above the price the store $\boxed{\text{paid}}$

for the item.

The **selling price** is the amount the $\boxed{\text{customer}}$ pays.

The amount by which a $\boxed{\text{regular price}}$ is $\boxed{\text{reduced}}$

is called the **discount**.

EXAMPLE Find the Selling Price

3 **MARKUP** Shirts bought by a sporting goods store cost them $20 per shirt. The want to mark them up 40%. What will be the selling price?

Find the amount of the markup. That is, find 40% of $20. Let *m* represent the markup.

$m = \boxed{0.40} \cdot 20$ Write 40% as a decimal.

$m = \boxed{8}$ Multiply.

Add the markup to the price they paid for the shirts.

$20 + \boxed{\$8} = \boxed{\$28}$

REMEMBER IT

There may be more than one way to solve a problem. See page 238 of your textbook for other methods you can use to solve Examples 3 and 4.

Your Turn Silk flowers bought by a craft store cost them $10 per yard. They want to mark them up 35 percent. What will be the selling price?

$13.50

EXAMPLE Find the Sale Price

4 **SHOPPING** A computer usually sells for $1,200. This week it is on sale for 30% off. What is the sale price?

Find 30% of $1,200. Let *d* represent the discount.

$d = \boxed{0.30} \cdot \boxed{1,200}$

$d = \boxed{360}$

Subtract the amount of the discount from the original price.

$1,200 - \boxed{\$360} = \boxed{\$840}$

Your Turn A DVD sells for $28. This week it is on sale for 20% off. What is the sale price?

$22.40

HOMEWORK ASSIGNMENT

Page(s):

Exercises:

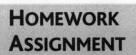

WHAT YOU'LL LEARN

- Solve problems involving simple interest.

BUILD YOUR VOCABULARY (pages 108–109)

Interest is the amount of money paid or [earned] for the use of money.

Principal is the amount of money [invested] or borrowed.

EXAMPLE   Find Simple Interest

1 **Find the simple interest for $2,000 invested at 5.5% for 4 years.**

$I = prt$ Write the simple interest formula.

$I = $ [**2,000**] · [**0.055**] · [**4**]   Replace p with [**2,000**], r with [**0.055**], and t with [**4**].

$I = $ [**440**]   The simple interest is [**$440**].

EXAMPLE   Find the Total Amount

2 **Find the total amount of money in an account where $80 is invested at 6% for 6 months.**

You need to find the total amount in an account. The time is given in months. Six months is $\frac{6}{12}$ or [$\frac{1}{2}$] year.

$I = prt$

$I = $ [**80**] · [**0.06**] · [$\frac{1}{2}$]

$I = $ [**2.4**]

The amount in the account is $80 + [**$2.40**] or [**$82.40**].

REMEMBER IT

The t in the simple interest formula represents time in years. If time is given in months, weeks, or days, the time must be changed to time in years.

Your Turn

a. Find the simple interest for $1,500 invested at 5% for 3 years.

$225

b. Find the total amount of money in an account where $60 is invested at 8% for 3 months.

$61.20

EXAMPLE Find the Interest Rate

3 **LOANS** Gerardo borrowed $4,500 from his bank for home improvements. He will repay the loan by paying $120 a month for the next four years. Find the simple interest rate of the loan.

First, find the total amount of money Gerardo will pay.

$120 · 48 = $5,760 .

He will pay $5,760 − $4,500 or $1,260 in interest.

The loan will be for 48 months or 4 years. Use the simple interest formula to find the interest rate.

$$I \quad = \quad p \quad \cdot r \cdot \quad t$$

$$1,260 = 4,500 \cdot r \cdot 4$$

$$1,260 = 18,000r \qquad \text{Simplify.}$$

$$\frac{1,260}{18,000} = \frac{1,800r}{18,000} \qquad \text{Divide each side by 18,000.}$$

$$0.07 = r \qquad \text{Simplify.}$$

The simple interest rate is 7% .

Your Turn Jocelyn borrowed $3,600 from her bank for home improvements. She will repay the loan by paying $90 a month for the next 5 years. Find the simple interest rate of the loan.

10%

HOMEWORK ASSIGNMENT

Page(s):

Exercises:

BRINGING IT ALL TOGETHER

STUDY GUIDE

FOLDABLES™	VOCABULARY PUZZLEMAKER	BUILD YOUR VOCABULARY
Use your **Chapter 5 Foldable** to help you study for your chapter test.	To make a crossword puzzle, word search, or jumble puzzle of the vocabulary words in Chapter 5, go to: www.glencoe.com/sec/math/t_resources/free/index.php	You can use your completed **Vocabulary Builder** *(pages 108–109)* to help you solve the puzzle.

5-1

Ratios and Percents

Write each ratio or fraction as a percent.

1. 21 out of 100

> **21%**

2. 4:10

> **40%**

3. $\frac{9}{25}$

> **36%**

Write each percent as a fraction in simplest form.

4. 27%

> $\frac{27}{100}$

5. 50%

> $\frac{1}{2}$

6. 0.8

> $\frac{4}{5}$

5-2

Fractions, Decimals, and Percents

Write each percent as a decimal.

7. 29%

> **0.29**

8. 376%

> **3.76**

9. 5%

> **0.05**

Write each decimal or fraction as a percent.

10. 3.9

> **390%**

11. $\frac{7}{8}$

> **87.5%**

12. $\frac{1}{3}$

> **33.3%**

5-3

The Percent Proportion

13. In a percent proportion, the **part** is being compared to

the whole quantity, called the **base** .

Solve.

14. What percent of 48 is 6?

12.5%

15. 14 is 20% of what number?

70

5-4

Finding Percents Mentally

Complete each statement.

16. 40% of 25 = $\boxed{\dfrac{2}{5}}$ of 25 or $\boxed{10}$

17. $\boxed{25\%}$ of 36 = $\frac{1}{4}$ of 36 or $\boxed{9}$

18. $66\frac{2}{3}\%$ of 48 = $\boxed{\dfrac{2}{3}}$ of 48 or $\boxed{32}$

19. $\boxed{10\%}$ of 89 = 0.1 of 89 or $\boxed{8.9}$

Compute mentally.

20. $33\frac{1}{3}\%$ of 300

100

21. 1% of 268

2.68

22. 25% of 120

30

5-5

Percent and Estimation

23. Are $\frac{1}{8}$ and 56 compatible numbers? Explain.

Yes, Sample answer: It is easy to divide 56 by 8.

24. Describe how to estimate 65% of 64 using compatible numbers.

65% is about $66\frac{2}{3}\%$ or $\frac{2}{3}$, and 64 is about 63. $\frac{1}{3}$ of 63 is 21 and 2 · 21 is 42. So 65% of 64 is about 42.

5-6
The Percent Equation

Write each percent proportion as a percent equation.

25. $\frac{16}{64} = \frac{25}{100}$ **16 = 0.25(64)**

26. $\frac{a}{14} = \frac{2}{100}$ ***a* = 0.02(14)**

27. $\frac{96}{b} = \frac{48}{100}$ **96 = 0.48*b***

28. $\frac{13}{100} = \frac{p}{675}$ ***p* = 0.13 (675)**

5-7
Percent of Change

Find the percent of change. Round to the nearest tenth if necessary. State whether the change is an *increase* or *decrease*.

29. Original: 29
New: 64

45.3%; increase

30. Original: 51
New: 42

1.2%; decrease

31. Find the selling price for the sweater.

Cost to store: $15
Mark up: 35%

$20.25

5-8
Simple Interest

Write *interest* or *principal* to complete each sentence.

32. **Interest** is the amount of money paid or earned for the use of money.

33. **Interest** equals **principal** times rate times time.

34. Find the total amount in the account where $560 is invested at 5.6% for 6 months.

First, find the **interest** earned.

Then, add the **interest** earned and the **principal** to find the total amount in the account.

What is the total amount for $560 at 5.6% for 6 months?

$575.68

ARE YOU READY FOR THE CHAPTER TEST?

Math Online

Visit **msmath3.net** to access your text book, more examples, self-check quizzes, and practice tests to help you study the concepts in Chapter 5.

Check the one that applies. Suggestions to help you study are given with each item.

☐ **I completed the review of all or most lessons without using my notes or asking for help.**

- You are probably ready for the Chapter Test.

- You may want to take the Chapter 5 Practice Test on page 249 of your textbook as a final check.

☐ **I used my Foldable or Study Notebook to complete the review of all or most lessons.**

- You should complete the Chapter 5 Study Guide and Review on pages 246–248 of your textbook.

- If you are unsure of any concepts or skills, refer back to the specific lesson(s).

- You may want to take the Chapter 5 Practice Test on page 249.

☐ **I asked for help from someone else to complete the review of all or most lessons.**

- You should review the examples and concepts in your Study Notebook and Chapter 5 Foldable.

- Then complete the Chapter 5 Study Guide and Review on pages 246–248 of your textbook.

- If you are unsure of any concepts or skills, refer back to the specific lesson(s).

- You may want to take the Chapter 5 Practice Test on page 249.

Student Signature

Parent/Guardian Signature

Teacher Signature

Geometry

 Use the instructions below to make a Foldable to help you organize your notes as you study the chapter. You will see Foldable reminders in the margin of this Interactive Study Notebook to help you in taking notes.

Begin with a plain piece of 11″ × 17″ paper.

STEP 1 **Fold**
Fold the paper in fifths lengthwise.

STEP 2 **Open and Fold**
Fold a $2\frac{1}{2}$" tab along the short side. Then fold the rest in half.

STEP 3 **Label**
Draw lines along folds and label each section as shown.

	words	model
lines		
polygons		
symmetry		
trans-formations		

 NOTE-TAKING TIP: When you read and learn new concepts, help yourself remember these concepts by taking notes, writing definitions and explanations, and draw models as needed.

Chapter 6

BUILD YOUR VOCABULARY

This is an alphabetical list of new vocabulary terms you will learn in Chapter 6. As you complete the study notes for the chapter, you will see Build Your Vocabulary reminders to complete each term's definition or description on these pages. Remember to add the textbook page number in the second column for reference when you study.

Vocabulary Term	Found on Page	Definition	Description or Example
acute triangle			
adjacent angles			
alternate exterior angles			
alternate interior angles			
complementary angles			
corresponding angles			
equilateral triangle			
isosceles triangle			
line symmetry			
obtuse triangle			

Vocabulary Term	Found on Page	Definition	Description or Example
parallelogram			
quadrilateral			
reflection			
rhombus			
right triangle			
rotation			
scalene triangle			
supplementary angles			
translation			
transversal			
trapezoid			
vertical angles			

Line and Angle Relationships

WHAT YOU'LL LEARN

• Identify special pairs of angles and relationships of angles formed by two parallel lines cut by a transversal.

KEY CONCEPTS

Special Pairs of Angles

Vertical angles are opposite angles formed by intersecting lines. Vertical angles are congruent.

Adjacent angles have the same vertex, share a common side, and do not overlap.

The sum of the measures of **supplementary angles** is 180°.

The sum of the measures of **complementary angles** is 90°.

BUILD YOUR VOCABULARY (pages 134–135)

Acute angles have measures less than $\boxed{90°}$.

Right angles have measures $\boxed{\text{equal}}$ to 90°.

Obtuse angles have measures between $\boxed{90°}$ and $\boxed{180°}$.

Straight angles have measures equal to $\boxed{180°}$.

EXAMPLES Classify Angles and Angle Pairs

Classify each angle or angle pair using all names that apply.

1

$m\angle 1$ is less than $\boxed{90°}$. So, $\angle 1$ is an $\boxed{\text{acute}}$ angle.

2

$\angle 1$ and $\angle 2$ are $\boxed{\text{adjacent}}$ angles since they have the same vertex, share a common side, and do not overlap. Together they form a straight angle measuring $\boxed{180°}$. So, $\angle 1$ and $\angle 2$ are $\boxed{\text{adjacent}}$ angles and $\boxed{\text{supplementary}}$ angles.

REMEMBER IT

Supplementary and complementary angles may or may not be adjacent angles.

Your Turn Classify each angle or angle pair using all names that apply.

a.

| right |

b.

| adjacent, complementary |

EXAMPLE Finding a Missing Angle Measure

3 The two angles below are supplementary. Find the value of x.

155° $x°$

$155 + x =$ 180   Definition of supplementary angles

$\boxed{-155}$ $=$ $\boxed{-155}$ Subtract $\boxed{155}$ from each side.

x $=$ 25   Simplify.

Your Turn The two angles shown are complementary. Find the value of x.

35

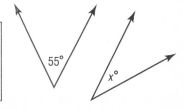

55° $x°$

KEY CONCEPT

If two parallel lines are cut by a transversal, then the following statements are true.

Alternate interior angles, those on opposite sides of the transversal and inside the other two lines, are congruent.

Alternate exterior angles, those on opposite sides of the transversal and outside the other two lines, are congruent.

Corresponding angles, those in the same position on the two lines in relation to the transversal, are congruent.

BUILD YOUR VOCABULARY (page 135)

Lines that intersect at $\boxed{\text{right}}$ angles are called **perpendicular lines.**

Two lines in a plane that never $\boxed{\text{intersect}}$ or cross are called **parallel lines.**

A **transversal** is a line that $\boxed{\text{intersects}}$ two or more lines.

ORGANIZE IT

Use sketches and words to define the lines and angles discussed in this lesson. Try to show relationships among different lines and angles. Write this in the "Lines" section of your Foldable table.

	words	model
lines		
polygons		
symmetry		
trans-formations		

EXAMPLE Find an Angle Measure

④ **BRIDGES** The sketch below shows a simple bridge design used in the 19th century. The top beam and floor of the bridge are parallel. If $m\angle 1 = 60°$ and $m\angle 3 = 45°$, find $m\angle 2$ and $m\angle 4$.

Since $\angle 2$ and $\angle 3$ are alternate interior angles, they are

| **congruent** | .

So, $m\angle 2 =$ | **45°** | .

Since $\angle 1$, $\angle 2$, and $\angle 4$ form a line, the sum of their measures

is | **180°** | . Therefore, $m\angle 4 = 180° -$ | **45°** | $- 60°$ or

| **75°** | .

Your Turn Refer to the sketch in Example 4. If $m\angle 1 = 45°$ and $m\angle 3 = 40°$, find $m\angle 2$ and $m\angle 4$.

$m\angle 2 = 40°$ and $m\angle 4 = 95°$

HOMEWORK ASSIGNMENT

Page(s):

Exercises:

Triangles and Angles

* Find the missing angle measures in triangles and classify triangles by their angles and sides.

KEY CONCEPT

Angles of a Triangle The sum of the measures of the angles of a triangle is 180°.

BUILD YOUR VOCABULARY (pages 134–135)

An **acute triangle** has | **three** | acute angles.

An **obtuse triangle** has one | **obtuse** | angle.

A **right triangle** has one | **right** | angle.

A **scalene triangle** has | **no congruent** | sides.

An **isosceles triangle** has at least | **two** | congruent sides.

An **equilateral triangle** has | **three** | congruent sides.

EXAMPLE   Find a Missing Angle Measure

1 Find the value of x in $\triangle PQR$.

$m\angle P + m\angle Q + m\angle R = 180$ The sum of the measures is 180.

| **17** | + | **46** | $+ x = 180$ Replace $m\angle P$ with 17, $m\angle Q$ with | **46** |, and $m\angle R$ with x.

| **63** | $+ x = 180$ Simplify.

$-$ | **63** | $-$ | **63** | Subtract | **63** | from each side.

$x = $ | **117** |

Your Turn   Find the value of x in $\triangle TRI$.

| **35** |

EXAMPLES Classify Triangles

Classify each triangle by its angles and its sides.

2

| Angles | △ABC has | **one** | right angle. |

| Sides | △ABC has | **two** | congruent sides. |

So, △ABC is a right **isosceles** triangle.

3

| Angles | △PQR has | **one** | obtuse angle. |

| Sides | △PQR has | **no** | congruent sides. |

So, △PQR is an obtuse **scalene** triangle.

Your Turn Classify each triangle by its angles and its sides.

a.

acute equilateral

b.

right scalene

Special Right Triangles

WHAT YOU'LL LEARN

• Find the missing measures in 30°-60° right triangles and 45°-45° right triangles.

EXAMPLE Find Lengths of a 30°-60° Right Triangle

1 **Find the missing lengths. Round to the nearest tenth if necessary.**

Step 1 Find c.

$$a = \frac{1}{2}c$$ Write the equation.

$$\boxed{6} = \frac{1}{2}c$$ Replace a with $\boxed{6}$.

$$\boxed{2} \cdot \boxed{6} = \boxed{2} \cdot \frac{1}{2}c$$ Multiply each side by $\boxed{2}$.

$$\boxed{12} = c$$ Simplify.

Step 2 Find b.

$$c^2 = a^2 + b^2$$ Pythagorean Theorem

$$\boxed{12^2} = \boxed{6^2} + b^2$$ $c = \boxed{12}$, $a = \boxed{6}$.

$$\boxed{144} = \boxed{36} + b^2$$ Evaluate $\boxed{12^2}$ and $\boxed{6^2}$.

$$\boxed{144} - \boxed{36} = \boxed{36} + b^2 - \boxed{36}$$ Subtract.

$$\boxed{108} = b^2$$ Simplify.

$$\boxed{\sqrt{108}} = \boxed{\sqrt{b^2}}$$ Take the square root of each side.

$$\boxed{10.4} \approx b$$ Use a calculator.

The length of b is about $\boxed{10.4}$ inches, and the length

of c is $\boxed{12}$ inches.

WRITE IT

What does the Pythagorean Theorem say about the relationship between the hypotenuse and the legs of a right triangle?

_____

_____

_____

_____

Your Turn Find each missing length. Round to the nearest tenth if necessary.

a = 10 cm, $b \approx$ 17.3 cm

EXAMPLE Find Lengths of a 45°-45° Right Triangle

2 **BASEBALL** The figure shows a baseball diamond. The distance between home plate and first base is 90 feet. The area between first base, third base, and home plate forms a 45°-45° right triangle. Find the distance from first base to third base and the distance from third base to home plate.

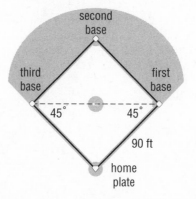

Let a equal the distance from home plate to third base.

Let b equal the distance from home plate to first base.

Let c equal the distance from first base to third base.

Step 1 Find a.

Sides a and b are the **same** length.

Since b = **90** feet, a = **90** feet.

Step 2   Find c.

$$c^2 = a^2 + b^2$$ **Pythagorean Theorem**

$$c^2 = \boxed{90}^2 + \boxed{90}^2$$ Replace a with $\boxed{90}$ and b with $\boxed{90}$.

$$c^2 = \boxed{8,100} + \boxed{8,100}$$ Evaluate $\boxed{90^2}$.

$$c^2 = \boxed{16,200}$$ Simplify.

$$\boxed{\sqrt{c^2}} = \boxed{\sqrt{16,200}}$$ Take the square root of each side.

$$\boxed{c} \approx \boxed{127.3}$$ Use a calculator.

The distance from first base to third base is about $\boxed{127}$ feet,

and the distance from third base to home plate is $\boxed{90}$ feet.

Your Turn   The sail of a sailboat is in the shape of a 45°-45° right triangle. The height of the sail is 12 feet. Find each missing length.

12 ft c

b

$b = 12$ ft; $c \approx 17$ ft

HOMEWORK ASSIGNMENT

Page(s):

Exercises:

Classifying Quadrilaterals

WHAT YOU'LL LEARN

- Find missing angle measures in quadrilaterals and classify quadrilaterals.

BUILD YOUR VOCABULARY (pages 134–135)

A **quadrilateral** is a polygon that has four sides and

 four angles.

KEY CONCEPT

Angles of a Quadrilateral
The sum of the measures of the angles of a quadrilateral is 360°.

EXAMPLE Find a Missing Angle Measure

1 Find the value of q in quadrilateral *PQRS*.

$m\angle P + m\angle Q + m\angle R + m\angle S =$ **360**   The sum of the measures is **360** .

124 $+ q +$ **36** $+$ **120** $=$ **360**   Replace the known angle measure and $m\angle Q$ with q.

280 $+ q =$ **360**   Simplify.

$-$ **280** $-$ **280**   Subtract **280** from each side.

$q =$ **80**   Simplify.

Your Turn Find the value of q in quadrilateral *QUAD*.

150

BUILD YOUR VOCABULARY (page 135)

A **trapezoid** is a quadrilateral with one pair of

| parallel | opposite sides.

A **parallelogram** is a quadrilateral with both pairs of

opposite sides | parallel | and | congruent |.

A **rhombus** is a quadrilateral with | four | congruent sides.

A **rectangle** is a parallelogram with 4 | right | angles.

A **square** is a parallelogram with 4 | congruent | sides

and 4 | right | angles.

EXAMPLES Classify Quadrilaterals

Classify each quadrilateral using the name that *best* describes it.

2

The quadrilateral has | no | congruent

sides and | no | special angles.

It is a | quadrilateral |.

3

The quadrilateral has | all | sides

congruent and | four | right angles.

It is a | square |.

FOLDABLES

ORGANIZE IT

Using sketches, symbols, and words, describe how to classify quadrilaterals. Add this to the "Polygons" section of your Foldable table.

	words	model
lines		
polygons		
symmetry		
transformations		

Your Turn **Classify each quadrilateral using the name that *best* describes it.**

a.

| rhombus |

b.

| rectangle |

© Glencoe/McGraw-Hill

HOMEWORK ASSIGNMENT

Page(s):

Exercises:

Mathematics: Applications and Concepts, Course 3   **145**

Congruent Polygons

WHAT YOU'LL LEARN

• Identify congruent polygons.

KEY CONCEPT

Congruent Polygons
If two polygons are congruent, their corresponding sides are congruent and their corresponding angles are congruent.

EXAMPLE **Identify Congruent Polygons**

1 Determine whether the trapezoids shown are congruent. If so, name the corresponding parts and write a congruence statement.

Angles   The arcs indicate that $\angle S \cong \angle G$,

$\angle T \cong \angle H$, $\angle Q \cong \angle E$, and $\boxed{\angle R \cong \angle F}$.

Sides   The side measures indicate that $\overline{ST} \cong \overline{GH}$,

$\overline{TQ} \cong \overline{HE}$, $\overline{QR} \cong \overline{EF}$, and $\boxed{\overline{RS} \cong \overline{FG}}$.

Since $\boxed{\text{all}}$ pairs of corresponding angles and sides are

$\boxed{\text{congruent}}$, the two trapezoids are $\boxed{\text{congruent}}$. One

congruence statement is trapezoid

$EFGH \cong$ trapezoid $\boxed{QRST}$.

Your Turn Determine whether the triangles shown are congruent. If so, name the corresponding parts and write a congruence statement.

$\boxed{\text{yes; } \overline{AB} \cong \overline{DE}, \overline{AC} \cong \overline{DF}, \overline{BC} \cong \overline{EF}; \angle A \cong D,}$
$\boxed{\angle B \cong E, \angle C \cong F; \triangle ABC \cong \triangle DEF}$

EXAMPLES Find Missing Measures

In the figure, $\triangle FGH \cong \triangle QRS$.

2 Find $m\angle S$.

According to the congruence statement, $\angle H$ and $\angle S$ are

corresponding angles. So, $\boxed{\angle H} \cong \boxed{\angle S}$.

Since $m\angle H = \boxed{35°}$, $m\angle S = \boxed{35°}$.

3 Find QR.

$\overline{FG}$ corresponds to $\boxed{\overline{QR}}$. So, $\boxed{\overline{FG}} \cong \boxed{\overline{QR}}$.

Since $FG = \boxed{6}$ centimeters, $QR = \boxed{6}$ centimeters.

Your Turn In the figure, $\triangle ABC \cong \triangle LMN$.

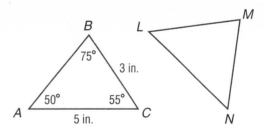

a. Find $m\angle N$.

$\boxed{55°}$

b. Find LN.

$\boxed{5 \text{ in.}}$

**HOMEWORK
ASSIGNMENT**

Page(s):

Exercises:

WHAT YOU'LL LEARN

- Identify line symmetry and rotational symmetry.

BUILD YOUR VOCABULARY (page 134)

A figure has **line symmetry** if it can be folded over a line so that one half of the figure | **matches** | the other half.

EXAMPLE Identify Line Symmetry

1 **TRILOBITES** The trilobite is an animal that lived millions of years ago. Determine whether the figure has line symmetry. If it does, draw all lines of symmetry. If not, write *none*.

This figure has | **one** | line of symmetry.

Your Turn Determine whether the leaf has line symmetry. If it does, draw all lines of symmetry. If not, write *none*.

| **1 line of symmetry** |

EXAMPLES Identify Rotational Symmetry

FLOWERS Determine whether each flower design has rotational symmetry. Write *yes* or *no*. If *yes*, name its angle(s) of rotation.

WRITE IT

How many degrees does one complete turn of a figure measure? Why is it this number of degrees?

_____

_____

_____

2

Yes, this figure has | **rotational** | symmetry.

It will match itself after being rotated 90°,

180°, and | **270°** | .

Yes, this figure has **rotational** symmetry.

It will match itself after being rotated **60°**,

120°, 180°, 240°, and **300°** .

FOLDABLES

ORGANIZE IT

Use sketches and words to show lines of symmetry and line symmetry. Write this in the "Symmetry" section of your Foldable table.

	words	model
lines		
polygons		
symmetry		
trans-formations		

Your Turn Determine whether the flower design has rotational symmetry. Write *yes* or *no*. If *yes*, name its angle(s) of rotation.

a.

yes; 180°

b.

no

HOMEWORK ASSIGNMENT

Page(s):

Exercises:

Reflections

WHAT YOU'LL LEARN

• Graph reflections on a coordinate plane.

BUILD YOUR VOCABULARY (page 135)

A **reflection** (sometimes called a *flip*) is a transformation in which a   **mirror**   image is produced by   **flipping**   a figure over a line.

EXAMPLE Draw a Reflection

KEY CONCEPT

Properties of Reflections

1. Every point on a reflection is the same distance from the line of reflection as the corresponding point on the original figure.

2. The image is congruent to the original figure, but the orientation of the image is *different* from that of the original figure.

1 Draw the image of trapezoid *STUV* after a reflection over the given line.

Step 1 Count the number of units between each vertex and the line of   **reflection** .

Step 2 Plot a point for each vertex the   **same**   distance away from the line on the other side.

Step 3 Connect the new   **vertices**   to form the image of trapezoid *STUV*, trapezoid *S'T'U'V'*.

Your Turn Draw the image of trapezoid *TRAP* after a reflection over the given line.

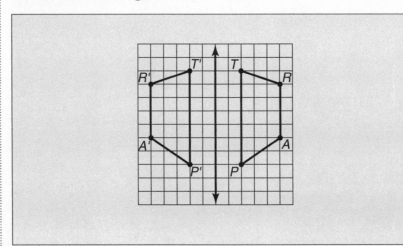

EXAMPLE Reflect a Figure over the *x*-axis

2 Graph quadrilateral *EFGH* with verticles *E*(−4, 4), *F*(3, 3), *G*(4, 2), and *H*(−2, 1). Then graph the image of *EFGH* after a reflection over the *x*-axis and write the coordinates of its vertices.

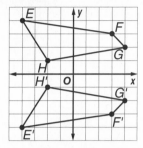

The coordinates of the verticles of the image are *E′* $(-4, -4)$,

F′ $(3, -3)$, *G′* $(4, -2)$ and *H′* $(-2, -1)$.

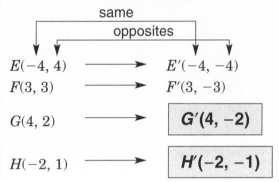

```
            same
            opposites

E(-4, 4)  ──────→  E'(-4, -4)
F(3, 3)   ──────→  F'(3, -3)

G(4, 2)   ──────→   G'(4, -2)

H(-2, 1)  ──────→   H'(-2, -1)
```

Notice that the *y*-coordinate of a point reflected over the *x*-axis

is the **opposite** of the *y*-coordinate of the original point.

Your Turn Graph quadrilateral *QUAD* with vertices *Q*(2, 4), *U*(4, 1), *A*(−1, 1), and *D*(−3, 3). Then graph the image of *QUAD* after a reflection over the *x*-axis, and write the coordinates of its vertices.

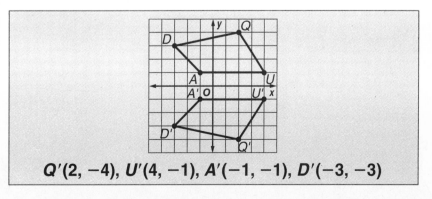

***Q′*(2, −4), *U′*(4, −1), *A′*(−1, −1), *D′*(−3, −3)**

EXAMPLE Reflect a Figure over the *y*-axis

3 Graph trapezoid *ABCD* with vertices *A*(1, 3), *B*(4, 0), *C*(3, −4), and *D*(1, −2). Then graph the image of *ABCD* after a reflection over the *y*-axis, and write the coordinates of its vertices.

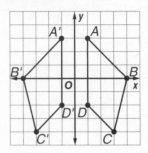

The coordinates of the vertices of the image are *A'* **(−1, 3)**,

B' **(−4, 0)**, *C'* **(−3, −4)**, and *D'* **(−1, −2)**.

| opposites |
| same |

A(1, 3)	*A'*(−1, 3)
B(4, 0)	*B'*(−4, 0)
C(3, −4)	**C'(−3, −4)**
D(1, −2)	**D'(−1, −2)**

Notice that the *x*-coordinate of a point reflected over the *y*-axis

is the opposite of the *x*-coordinate of the **original** point.

Your Turn Graph quadrilateral *ABCD* with vertices *A*(2, 2), *B*(5, 0), *C*(4, −2), and *D*(2, −1). Then graph the image of *ABCD* after a reflection over the *y*-axis, and write the coordinates of its vertices.

***A'*(−2, 2), *B'*(−5, 0), *C'*(−4, −2), *D'*(−2, −1).**

HOMEWORK ASSIGNMENT

Page(s):

Exercises:

Translations

WHAT YOU'LL LEARN

- Graph translations on a coordinate plane.

© Glencoe/McGraw-Hill

BUILD YOUR VOCABULARY (page 135)

A **translation** (sometimes called a *slide*) is the

| movement | of a figure from one position to another

| without | turning it.

KEY CONCEPT

Properties of Translations

1. Every point on the original figure is moved the same distance and in the same direction.

2. The image is congruent to the original figure, and the orientation of the image is *the same* as that of the original figure.

EXAMPLE Draw a Translation

1 Draw the image of △*EFG* after a translation of 3 units right and 2 units up.

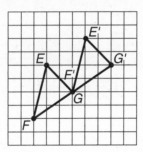

Step 1 Move each vertex of the triangle **3** units right and **2** units up.

Step 2 Connect the new vertices to form the **image** .

Your Turn Draw the image of △*ABC* after a translation of 2 units right and 4 units down.

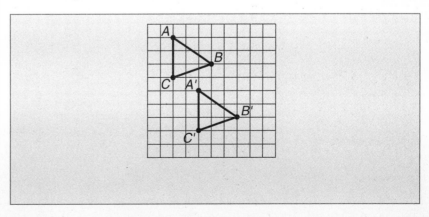

EXAMPLE Translation in the Coordinate Plane

2 Graph △*ABC* with vertices *A*(−2, 2), *B*(3, 4), and *C*(4, 1). Then graph the image of △*ABC* after a translation of 2 units left and 5 units down. Write the coordinates of its vertices.

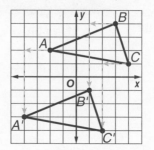

The coordinates of the vertices of the image are

A' $(-4, -3)$, *B'* $(1, -1)$, and *C'* $(2, -4)$. Notice

that these vertices can also be found by adding -2 to the

x-coordinates and -5 to the *y*-coordinates, or (−2, −5).

Original	Add (−2, −5)	Image
A(−2, 2) ⟶	(−2 + (−2), 2 + (−5)) ⟶	$(-4, -3)$
B(3, 4) ⟶	(3 + (−2), 4 + (−5)) ⟶	$(1, -1)$
C(4, 1) ⟶	(4 + (−2), 1 + (−5)) ⟶	$(2, -4)$

Your Turn Graph △*PQR* with vertices *P*(−1, 3), *Q*(2, 4), and *R*(3, 2). Then graph the image of △*PQR* after a translation of 2 units left and 3 units down. Write the coordinates of its vertices.

P'(1, 0), *Q'*(4, 1), *R'*(5, −1)

ORGANIZE IT

Draw a triangle or simple quadrilateral on graph paper. Then draw a translation. Show how you determined the points needed to graph the translated figure. Put your work in the "Transformations" section of your Foldable table.

	words	model
lines		
polygons		
symmetry		
trans-formations		

HOMEWORK ASSIGNMENT

Page(s):

Exercises:

Rotations

WHAT YOU'LL LEARN

• Graph rotations on a coordinate plane.

BUILD YOUR VOCABULARY (page 135)

A **rotation** (sometimes called a *turn*) is a transformation involving the | **turning** | or spinning of a figure around a fixed point.

KEY CONCEPT

Properties of Rotations

1. Corresponding points are the same distance from *R*. The angles formed by connecting *R* to corresponding points are congruent.

2. The image is congruent to the original figure, and their orientations are *the same*.

EXAMPLE Rotations in the Coordinate Plane

1 Graph △*QRS* with vertices *Q*(1, 1), *R*(3, 4), and *S*(4, 1). Then graph the image of △*QRS* after a rotation of 180° counterclockwise about the origin, and write the coordinates of its vertices.

Step 1 Lightly draw a line connecting point *Q* to the | **origin** |.

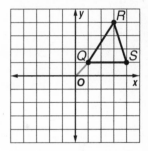

Step 2 Lightly draw $\overline{OQ'}$ so that $m\angle Q'OQ = 180°$ and $OQ' = OQ$.

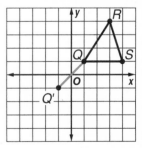

Step 3 Repeat steps 1–3 for points *R* and *Q*. Then erase all lightly drawn lines and connect the | **vertices** | to form △*Q'R'S'*.

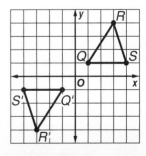

Triangle *Q'R'S'* has vertices

Q' | **(−1, −1)** |, *R'* | **(−3, −4)** |, and *S'* | **(−4, −1)** |.

ORGANIZE IT

Draw a triangle on graph paper. Then draw a rotation. Label the rotation with degrees and direction of rotation. Put your work in the "Transformations" section of your Foldable table.

	words	model
lines		
polygons		
symmetry		
trans-formations		

Your Turn Graph △ABC with vertices A(4, 1), B(2, 1), and C(2, 4). Then graph the image of △ABC after a rotation of 180° counterclockwise about the origin, and write the coordinates of its vertices.

$A'(-4, -1)$, $B'(-2, -1)$, $C'(-2, -4)$

EXAMPLE Use a Rotation

2 QUILTS Complete the quilt piece shown below so that the completed figure has rotational symmetry with 90°, 180°, and 270°, as its angles of rotation.

Rotate the figure 90°, 180°, and 270° counterclockwise. Use a

90° rotation *clockwise* to produce the same rotation as a 270° rotation *counterclockwise*.

90° counterclockwise   180°counterclockwise   90° clockwise

Your Turn Complete the quilt piece shown below so that the completed figure has rotational symmetry with 90°, 180°, and 270°, as its angles of rotation.

HOMEWORK ASSIGNMENT

Page(s):

Exercises:

BRINGING IT ALL TOGETHER

STUDY GUIDE

FOLDABLES™	VOCABULARY PUZZLEMAKER	BUILD YOUR VOCABULARY
Use your **Chapter 6 Foldable** to help you study for your chapter test.	To make a crossword puzzle, word search, or jumble puzzle of the vocabulary words in Chapter 6, go to www.glencoe.com/sec/math/t_resources/free/index.php.	You can use your completed **Vocabulary Builder** (*pages 134–135*) to help you solve the puzzle.

6-1

Line and Angle Relationships

Match each figure to the words that describe it.

1. obtuse   d

2. right   b

3. acute   a

4. straight   c

5. 180°   c

6. 90°   b

a.

b.

c.

d.

7. How do you know if two lines are perpendicular?

> **Sample answer: The lines will intersect at right angles.**

For Questions 8–10, use the figure at the right.

8. Look at $\angle 5$ and $\angle 6$. Classify the angle pair using all names that apply.

> **adjacent, supplementary**

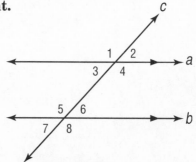

9. Find $m\angle 3$ if $m\angle 2 = 60°$.   **60°**

10. Find $m\angle 4$ if $m\angle 2 = 60°$.   **120°**

6-2

Triangles and Angles

11. How can you determine whether a triangle is a right triangle?

> **Sample answer: If the triangle has a 90° angle, then it is a right triangle.**

12. If one angle of a triangle is either right or obtuse, what must be true of the other two angles?

> **They must both be acute.**

13. Complete the table.

Type of Triangle	Number of Congruent Sides
Scalene	**none**
Isosceles	**at least two**
Equilateral	**three**

14. Triangle *RST* is an equilateral triangle. What is the measure of angle *T*? How do you know?

> **60°; all the angles are congruent and the sum of the angles must be 180°.**

6-3

Special Right Angles

15. The two legs in a 45°-45° right triangle are always congruent. Why?

> **Sample answer: The two angle measures are the same, so the triangle is isosceles. Thus, the lengths of the legs are always the same.**

16. Triangle *FGH* is a 45°-45° right triangle. The shorter side is 18 inches. Find the length of the longest side, rounded to the nearest tenth.

> **about 25.5 in.**

6-4

Classifying Quadrilaterals

17. Refer to the quadrilateral shown. Explain how to find the value of *y* in quadrilateral *ABCD*.

> **Add the known angle measures and then subtract the sum from 360°.**

18. What is the value of *y*?

> **120**

6-5

Congruent Polygons

19. Complete the sentence. Two polygons are congruent if their

corresponding sides are congruent and the

corresponding angles are **congruent** .

△*ABC* ≅ △*DEF*. *m*∠*A* = 40° and *m*∠*B* = 50°
∠*E* ≅ ∠*A* and ∠*F* ≅ ∠*C*

20. What is *m*∠*C*?

> **90°**

21. What is *m*∠*D*?

> **50°**

6-6

Symmetry

Write whether each sentence is *true* or *false*. If *false*, replace the underlined words to make a true sentence.

22. A figure has line symmetry if it can be <u>folded over a line</u> so that one half of the figure matches the other half.

> **true**

23. To rotate a figure means to turn the figure from its <u>center</u>.

> **true**

24. A figure has rotational symmetry if it first matches itself after being rotated <u>exactly</u> 360°.

> **false, less than**

6-7

Reflections

25. Complete. A reflection is a [**mirror**] image of a figure produced by flipping the figure over a line.

26. If you graphed quadrilateral *HIJK* reflected over the *y*-axis, what would be the coordinates of these vertices:

H′([**−1, 1**])   *J*′([**−4, 2**])

6-8

Translations

27. Complete. A translation is the movement of a figure from one position to another [**without**] turning it.

28. If you graphed the image of quadrilateral *DEFG* after a translation 3 units right and 4 units down, what would be the coordinates of these vertices:

D′([**1, −1**])   *F*′([**5, −2**])

6-9

Rotations

29. Find the distance of each of the vertices *A*, *B*, *A*′, and *B*′ from the given point. Are corresponding vertices, such as *A* and *A*′, the same distance from the point?

> ***A:*** 3 units, ***B:*** 1 unit, ***A*′:** 1 unit,
> ***B*′:** 3 units; no

30. Is quadrilateral *A*′*B*′*C*′*D*′ a rotation of quadrilateral *ABCD* about the given point? Why or why not?

> **No; corresponding vertices on the quadrilaterals are not the same distance from the point.**

ARE YOU READY FOR THE CHAPTER TEST?

Visit **msmath3.net** to access your textbook, more examples, self-check quizzes, and practice tests to help you study the concepts in Chapter 6.

Check the one that applies. Suggestions to help you study are given with each item.

☐ **I completed the review of all or most lessons without using my notes or asking for help.**

- You are probably ready for the Chapter Test.

- You may want to take the Chapter 6 Practice Test on page 309 of your textbook as a final check.

☐ **I used my Foldable or Study Notebook to complete the review of all or most lessons.**

- You should complete the Chapter 6 Study Guide and Review on pages 306–308 of your textbook.

- If you are unsure of any concepts or skills, refer to the specific lesson(s).

- You may also want to take the Chapter 6 Practice Test on page 309.

☐ **I asked for help from someone else to complete the review of all or most lessons.**

- You should review the examples and concepts in your Study Notebook and Chapter 6 Foldable.

- Then complete the Chapter 6 Study Guide and Review on pages 306–308 of your textbook.

- If you are unsure of any concepts or skills, refer to the specific lesson(s).

- You may also want to take the Chapter 6 Practice Test on page 309.

Student Signature

Parent/Guardian Signature

Teacher Signature

Geometry: Measuring Area and Volume

 Use the instructions below to make a Foldable to help you organize your notes as you study the chapter. You will see Foldable reminders in the margin of this Interactive Study Notebook to help you in taking notes.

Begin with a plain piece of $8\frac{1}{2}"\times 11"$ paper.

STEP 1   **Fold**
Fold in half widthwise.

STEP 2   **Open and Fold Again**
Fold the bottom to form a pocket. Glue edges.

STEP 3   **Label**
Label each pocket. Place several index cards in each pocket.

 NOTE-TAKING TIP: As you read and learn a new concept, such as how to measure area or volume, write examples and explanations showing the main ideas of the concept.

Chapter 7

BUILD YOUR VOCABULARY

This is an alphabetical list of new vocabulary terms you will learn in Chapter 7. As you complete the study notes for the chapter, you will see Build Your Vocabulary reminders to complete each term's definition or description on these pages. Remember to add the textbook page number in the second column for reference when you study.

Vocabulary Term	Found on Page	Definition	Description or Example
circumference			
complex figure			
cone			
cylinder			
diameter			
edge			
face			
lateral area			
lateral face			

Vocabulary Term	Found on Page	Definition	Description or Example
polyhedron			
precision			
prism			
pyramid			
radius			
significant digits			
slant height			
surface area			
vertex			
volume			

Area of Parallelograms, Triangles, and Trapezoids

© Glencoe/McGraw-Hill

WHAT YOU'LL LEARN

- Find the areas of parallelograms, triangles, and trapezoids.

KEY CONCEPT

Area of a Parallelogram, Triangle, and Trapezoid

Area of a Parallelogram The area A of a parallelogram is the product of any base b and its height h.

Area of a Triangle The area A of a triangle is half the product of any base b and its height h.

Area of a Trapezoid The area A of a trapezoid is half the product of the height h, and the sum of the bases b_1 and b_2.

EXAMPLE Find the Area of a Parallelogram

1 Find the area of the parallelogram.

2 cm   3 cm
7 cm

The base is $\boxed{7}$ centimeters. The height is $\boxed{2}$ centimeters.

$A = bh$ Area of a $\boxed{\textbf{parallelogram}}$

$A = \boxed{7} \cdot \boxed{2}$ Replace b with $\boxed{7}$ and h with $\boxed{2}$.

$A = \boxed{14}$ Multiply.

The area is $\boxed{14}$ square centimenters.

EXAMPLE Find the Area of a Triangle

2 Find the area of the triangle.

7 in.   4 in.
22 in.

The base is $\boxed{22}$ inches. The height is $\boxed{4}$ inches.

$A = \frac{1}{2}bh$ Area of a $\boxed{\textbf{triangle}}$

$A = \frac{1}{2}(\boxed{22})(\boxed{4})$ Replace b with $\boxed{22}$ and h with $\boxed{4}$.

$A = \frac{1}{2}(\boxed{88})$ Multiply. $22 \times 4 = \boxed{88}$

$A = \boxed{44}$ Multiply. $\frac{1}{2} \times 88 = \boxed{44}$

The area is $\boxed{44}$ square inches.

FOLDABLES

ORGANIZE IT

On index cards, write the formula for the area of a parallelogram, a triangle, and a trapezoid. Sketch each figure and label the parts. Place your cards in the "Area" pocket of your Foldable.

Your Turn Find the area of each figure.

a.

3 in.
4 in.
6 in.

18 in²

b.

7 in.
5 in.
12 in.

30 in²

EXAMPLE Find the Area of a Trapezoid

3 Find the area of the trapezoid.

The height is **3.4** yards. The lengths

of the bases are **5** yards and **1** yard.

4.5 yd
5 yd
3.4 yd
1 yd

$A = \frac{1}{2}h(b_1 + b_2)$ Area of a **trapezoid**

$A = \frac{1}{2}($ **3.4** $)(5 + 1)$ Replace h with **3.4**,

b_1 with 5, and b_2 with 1.

$A = \frac{1}{2}($ **3.4** $)($ **6** $)$ or **10.2**   Simplify.

The area of the trapezoid is **10.2** square yards.

Your Turn Find the area of the trapezoid.

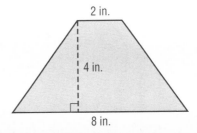

2 in.
4 in.
8 in.

20 in²

HOMEWORK ASSIGNMENT

Page(s):

Exercises:

Circumference and Area of Circles

WHAT YOU'LL LEARN

- Find the circumference and the area of circles.

BUILD YOUR VOCABULARY (pages 164–165)

The **radius** of a circle is the distance from the ┃ center ┃

to any point ┃ on ┃ the circle.

The **diameter** of a circle is the ┃ distance across ┃ the circle through the center.

The **circumference** of a circle is the ┃ distance around ┃ the circle.

EXAMPLES Find the Circumferences of Circles

Find the circumference of each circle. Round to the nearest tenth.

KEY CONCEPTS

Circumference of a Circle The circumference C of a circle is equal to its diameter d times π, or 2 times its radius r times π.

Area of a Circle The area A of a circle is equal to π times the square of the radius r.

1.

5 ft

$C = \boxed{\pi d}$ Circumference of a circle

$C = \boxed{\pi} \cdot \boxed{5}$ Replace d with $\boxed{5}$.

$C = \boxed{5\pi}$ This is the exact circumference.

Use a calculator to find 5π.

5 ⊠ × ⊠ π ⊠ ENTER = ⊠   15.70796327

The circumference is about ┃ **15.7 feet** ┃ .

2.

3.8 m

$C = \boxed{2\pi r}$ Circumference of a circle

$C = 2 \cdot \pi \cdot \boxed{3.8}$ Replace r with $\boxed{3.8}$.

$C \approx \boxed{23.9}$ Use a calculator.

The circumference is about ┃ **23.9 meters** ┃ .

Your Turn Find the circumference of each circle. Round to the nearest tenth.

a.

7 in.

22.0 in.

b.

3.6 m

22.6 m

EXAMPLES Find the Areas of Circles

Find the area of each circle. Round to the nearest tenth.

3

3 yd

$A = \boxed{\pi r^2}$ Area of a circle

$A = \pi \cdot \boxed{3}^2$ Replace r with $\boxed{3}$.

$A = \pi \cdot \boxed{9}$ Evaluate 3^2.

$A \approx \boxed{28.3}$ Use a calculator.

The area is about $\boxed{\textbf{28.3 square yards}}$.

4
10 in.

$A = \pi r^2$ Area of a circle

$A = \pi \cdot \boxed{5}^2$ $r = \frac{1}{2}$ of 10

$A = \pi \cdot \boxed{25}$ Evaluate 5^2.

$A \approx \boxed{78.5}$ Use a calculator.

The area is about $\boxed{\textbf{78.5 square inches}}$.

Your Turn Find the area of each circle. Round to the nearest tenth.

a.

2 ft

12.6 ft²

b.

8 cm

50.3 cm²

Area of Complex Figures

WHAT YOU'LL LEARN

• Find the area of complex figures.

BUILD YOUR VOCABULARY (pages 164–165)

A **complex figure** is made up of | **two or more** | shapes.

EXAMPLES Find the Areas of Complex Figures

Find the area of each complex figure. Round to the nearest tenth if necessary.

1

11 in.

5 in.

7 in.

2 in.

The figure can be separated into a | **rectangle** | and two

congruent | **triangles** | .

Area of rectangle

$A = \ell w$

$A = $ | **(7)(5)** |

$A = $ | **35** |

Area of one triangle

$A = \frac{1}{2}bh$

$A = $ | $\frac{1}{2} \cdot 5 \cdot 2$ |

$A = $ | **5** |

The area of the figure is | **35** | + | **5** | + | **5** | or | **45** | square inches.

---

12 cm

6 cm

The figure can be separated into two **semicircles** and

a **rectangle** .

Area of one semicircle

$A = \frac{1}{2}\pi r^2$

$A = \boxed{\frac{1}{2} \cdot \pi \cdot 3^2}$

$A \approx \boxed{14.1}$

Area of rectangle

$A = \ell w$

$A = \boxed{(12)(6)}$

$A = \boxed{72}$

The area of the figure is about 14.1 + $\boxed{14.1}$ + $\boxed{72}$ or

100.3 square centimeters.

Your Turn Find the area of each complex figure.
Round to the nearest tenth if necessary.

a.

16 in.

4 in.

7 in.

6 in.

70 in²

b.

2 ft

7 ft

17.1 ft²

**HOMEWORK
ASSIGNMENT**

Page(s):

Exercises:

WHAT YOU'LL LEARN

- Identify and draw three-dimensional figures.

KEY CONCEPT

Common Polyhedrons

triangular prism

rectangular prism

triangular pyramid

rectangular pyramid

BUILD YOUR VOCABULARY (pages 164–165)

A **polyhedron** is a solid with   flat   surfaces that are   polygons .

An **edge** is where two planes   intersect   in a line.

A **face** is a   flat   surface.

A **vertex** is where three or more planes   intersect   at a point.

A **prism** is a polyhedron with two   parallel, congruent   faces, or bases.

A **pyramid** is a polyhedron with one base that is a   polygon   and faces that are   triangles .

EXAMPLE Identify Prisms and Pyramids

Identify each solid. Name the number and shapes of the faces. Then name the number of edges and vertices.

1

The figure has two parallel   congruent   bases that are   octagons , so it is an   octagonal   prism. The other faces are rectangles. It has a total of   10   faces,   24   edges, and   16   vertices.

2 The figure has one base that is a **rectangle**,

so it is a **rectangular pyramid** .

The other faces are triangles. It has a total

of **5** faces, **8** edges, and **5** vertices.

Your Turn Identify each solid. Name the number and shapes of the faces. Then name the number of edges and vertices.

a.

triangular prism;
2 triangular faces,
3 rectangular faces,
9 edges, and 6 vertices

b.

pentagonal pyramid;
1 pentagonal base,
5 triangular faces,
10 edges, and 6 vertices

EXAMPLES Analyze Real-Life Drawings

ARCHITECTURE The plans for a hotel fireplace are shown at the right.

3 Draw and label the top, front, and side views.

top view

front view

side view

4 **Each unit on the drawing represents 1.5 feet. Find the area of the floor covered by the fireplace.**

You can see from the front view that the floor is a rectangle

that is ┃ 5 ┃ units wide by ┃ 6 ┃ units long. The actual

dimensions are ┃ 5 ┃ (1.5) feet by ┃ 6 ┃ (1.5) feet or 7.5 feet

by 9 feet.

$A = 7.5 \cdot 9$ $\qquad$ $A = \ell \cdot w$

$A = 67.5$ $\qquad$ Simplify.

The area of the floor covered by the fireplace is

┃ **67.5 square feet** ┃ .

┃ **Your Turn** ┃ **The plans for a building are shown to the right.**

a. Draw and label the top, front, and side views.

top view   front view   side view

© Glencoe/McGraw-Hill

b. Each unit on the drawing represents 150 feet. Find the area covered by the second floor.

225,000 ft²

HOMEWORK ASSIGNMENT

Page(s):

Exercises:

Volume of Prisms and Cylinders

BUILD YOUR VOCABULARY (pages 164–165)

WHAT YOU'LL LEARN

• Find the volumes of prisms and cylinders.

Volume is the measure of the ▢ space ▢ occupied by a solid. Volume is measured in cubic units.

EXAMPLE Find the Volume of a Rectangular Prism

① Find the volume of the prism.

KEY CONCEPT

Volume of a Prism The volume V of a prism is the area of the base B times the height h.

$V = Bh$ Volume of a prism

$V = \left(\boxed{\ell \cdot w} \right) h$ The base is a rectangle, so $B = \boxed{\ell \cdot w}$.

$V = (5 \cdot 7)11$ $\ell = 5, w = 7, h = 11$

$V = \boxed{385}$ Simplify.

The volume is 385 ▢ cubic ▢ inches.

5 in.
7 in.
11 in.

EXAMPLE Find the Volume of a Triangular Prism

② Find the volume of the prism.

$V = Bh$ Volume of a prism

$V = \left(\dfrac{1}{2} \cdot 9 \cdot 15 \right) h$ The base is a ▢ triangle ▢, so $B = \dfrac{1}{2} \cdot 9 \cdot 15$.

$V = \left(\dfrac{1}{2} \cdot 9 \cdot 15 \right) 4$ The height of the prism is ▢ 4 ▢.

$V = \boxed{270}$ Simplify.

The volume is ▢ 270 ▢ cubic inches.

9 ft
15 ft
4 ft

Your Turn Find the volume of each prism.

a.

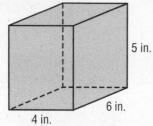

5 in.

6 in.

4 in.

b.

6 ft

3 ft

5 ft

| 120 in³ | | 45 ft³ |

BUILD YOUR VOCABULARY (pages 164–165)

A **cylinder** is a solid whose bases are congruent, parallel,

| circles |, connected with a | curved | side.

EXAMPLES Find the Volumes of Cylinders

Find the volume of each cylinder. Round to the nearest tenth if necessary.

KEY CONCEPT

Volume of a Cylinder
The volume V of a cylinder with radius r is the area of the base B times the height h.

3

3 cm

12 cm

$V = \pi r^2 h$ Volume of a cylinder

$V = \pi \cdot \boxed{3}^2 \cdot \boxed{12}$ $r = \boxed{3}$, $h = \boxed{12}$

$V \approx \boxed{339.3}$ Simplify.

The volume is about 339.3 | **cubic** | centimeters.

4 diameter of base, 18 yd; height, 25.4 yd

Since the diameter is 18 yards, the radius is | **9** | yards.

$V = \pi r^2 h$ Volume of a cylinder

$V = \pi \cdot \boxed{9}^2 \cdot \boxed{25.4}$ $r = \boxed{9}$, $h = \boxed{25.4}$

$V \approx \boxed{6{,}463.5}$ Simplify.

The volume is | **about 6,463.5 cubic yards** |.

ORGANIZE IT

On index cards, write the formula for the volume of a rectangular prism, a triangular prism, and a cylinder. Sketch each figure and label its parts. Place your cards in the "Volume" pocket of your Foldable.

Your Turn Find the volume of each cylinder. Round to the nearest tenth if necessary.

a.

169.6 in^3

b. diameter of base, 8 yd; height, 10 yd

502.7 yd^3

EXAMPLE Find the Volume of a Complex Solid

5 **TOYS** A wooden block has a single hole drilled entirely though it. What is the volume of the block? Round to the nearest hundredth.

The block is a rectangular prism with a cylindrical hole. To find the volume of the block, subtract the volume of the cylinder from the volume of the prism.

Rectangular Prism

$V = \boxed{Bh}$

$V = (6 \cdot 3)4$ or 72

Cylinder

$V = \boxed{\pi r^2 h}$

$V = \pi(1)^2(3)$ or 9.42

The volume of the box is about $\boxed{72} - \boxed{9.42}$ or $\boxed{62.58}$ 62.58 cubic centimeters.

Your Turn A small wooden cube has been glued to a larger wooden block for a whittling project. What is the volume of the wood to be whittled?

98 in^3

HOMEWORK ASSIGNMENT

Page(s):

Exercises:

Volume of Pyramids and Cones

WHAT YOU'LL LEARN

• Find the volumes of pyramids and cones.

KEY CONCEPT

Volume of a Pyramid
The volume V of a pyramid is one-third the area of the base B times the height h.

EXAMPLE Find the Volume of a Pyramid

1 **Find the volume of the pyramid.**

20 cm
7 cm
3 cm

$V = \frac{1}{3}Bh$ Volume of a pyramid

$V = \frac{1}{3}\left(\boxed{7} \cdot \boxed{3}\right)\boxed{20}$ $B = \boxed{7} \cdot \boxed{3}$,

                  $h = \boxed{20}$

$V = 140$ Simplify.

The volume is   **140 cubic centimeters** .

Your Turn Find the volume of the pyramid.

80 m²

12 m
4 m
5 m

EXAMPLE Use Volume to Solve a Problem

2 **SOUVENIRS** A novelty souvenir company wants to make snow globes shaped like a pyramid. It decides that the most cost-effective maximum volume of water for the pyramids is 12 cubic inches. If a pyramid globe measures 4 inches in height, find the area of its base.

$V = \frac{1}{3}Bh$ Volume of a pyramid

$\boxed{12} = \frac{1}{3} \cdot B \cdot 4$ Replace V with $\boxed{12}$ and h with $\boxed{4}$.

$12 = \frac{4}{3} \cdot B$ Simplify.

$\boxed{\frac{3}{4}} \cdot 12 = \boxed{\frac{3}{4}} \cdot \frac{4}{3} \cdot B$ Multiply each side by $\boxed{\frac{3}{4}}$.

$\boxed{9} = B$

The area of the base of the snow globe is 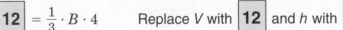 **9 square inches** .

Your Turn A company is designing pyramid shaped building blocks with a square base. They want the volume of the blocks to be 18 square inches. If the length of the side of the base is 3 inches, what should be the height of the blocks?

6 in.

KEY CONCEPT

Volume of a Cone
The volume *V* of a cone with radius *r* is one-third the area of the base *B* times the height *h*.

BUILD YOUR VOCABULARY (pages 164–165)

A **cone** is a three-dimensional figure with one **circular** base. A curved surface connects the base and the **vertex** .

EXAMPLE Find the Volume of a Cone

3 **Find the volume of the cone. Round to the nearest tenth.**

$V = \frac{1}{3}\pi r^2 h$ Volume of a cone

$V = \frac{1}{3} \cdot \pi \cdot \boxed{1.5}^2 \cdot \boxed{8}$ Replace *r* with $\boxed{1.5}$ and *h* with $\boxed{8}$.

$V \approx \boxed{18.8}$ Simplify.

The volume is $\boxed{\text{about 18.8 cubic meters}}$.

8 m

3 m

FOLDABLES

ORGANIZE IT

On index cards, write the formula for the volume of a pyramid and a cone. Sketch each figure and label its parts. Place your cards in the "Volume" pocket of your Foldable.

Area   Volume

Your Turn Find the volume of the cone. Round to the nearest tenth.

37.7 in³

9 in.

2 in.

HOMEWORK ASSIGNMENT

Page(s):
Exercises:

Surface Area of Prisms and Cylinders

WHAT YOU'LL LEARN

• Find the surface areas of prisms and cylinders.

BUILD YOUR VOCABULARY (pages 164–165)

The **surface area** of a solid is the | **sum** | of the

| **areas** | of all its | **surfaces** |, or faces.

EXAMPLE Surface Area of a Rectangular Prism

1 Find the surface area of the rectangular prism.

7 mm
15 mm   9 mm

KEY CONCEPT

Surface Area of a Rectangular Prism The surface area S of a rectangular prism with length ℓ, width w, and height h is the sum of the areas of the faces.

$S = 2\boxed{\ell w} + 2\boxed{\ell h} + 2\boxed{wh}$ Write the formula.

$S = 2(15)(9) + 2(15)(7) + 2(9)(7)$ Substitution

$S = \boxed{606}$ Simplify.

The surface area is $\boxed{606 \text{ square millimeters}}$.

Your Turn Find the surface area of the rectangular prism.

3 cm
7 cm
5 cm

142 cm²

Mathematics: Applications and Concepts, Course 3

EXAMPLE Surface Area of a Triangular Prism

© Glencoe/McGraw-Hill

REVIEW IT

What is the formula for finding the area of a triangle? How does this relate to finding the surface area of a triangular prism? *(Lesson 7-1)*

_____

_____

_____

_____

2 CAMPING A family wants to reinforce the fabric of its tent with a waterproofing treatment. Find the surface area, including the floor, of the tent below.

6.3 ft
5.8 ft
5 ft
5.8 ft

A triangular prism consists of two congruent ⬜ **triangular** faces and three ⬜ **rectangular** faces.

Draw and label a net of this prism. Find the area of each face.

bottom   **5** · **5.8** = 29

left side   **6.3** · **5.8** = 36.54

right side   **6.3** · **5.8** = 36.54

two bases $2\left(\frac{1}{2} \cdot 5 \cdot \boxed{5.8}\right) = 29$

The surface area of the tent is 29 + 36.54 + 36.54 + 29

or about **131.1 square feet**.

5.8 ft
6.3 ft   6.3 ft
5 ft
5.8 ft
5 ft
5.8 ft

FOLDABLES

ORGANIZE IT

On index cards, write these formulas for finding surface area. Then sketch and label each figure. Place the cards in the "Area" pocket of your Foldable.

Your Turn Julia is painting triangular prisms to use as decoration in her garden. Find the surface area of the prism.

85.5 in²

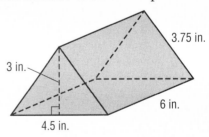
3.75 in.
3 in.
6 in.
4.5 in.

EXAMPLE Surface Area of a Cylinder

3 Find the surface area of the cylinder. Round to the nearest tenth.

$S = 2\pi r^2 + 2\pi rh$ Surface area of a cylinder

$S = 2\pi\left(\boxed{2.5} \right)^2 + 2\pi\left(\boxed{2.5} \right)\left(\boxed{2} \right)$ Replace r with $\boxed{2.5}$

and h with $\boxed{2}$.

$S \approx \boxed{70.7}$ Simplify.

The surface area is about $\boxed{70.7}$ square meters.

Your Turn Find the surface area of the cylinder. Round to the nearest tenth.

207.3 mm²

7-8 — **Surface Area of Pyramids and Cones**

WHAT YOU'LL LEARN

- Find the surface areas of pyramids and cones.

BUILD YOUR VOCABULARY (pages 164–165)

The   triangular sides   of a pyramid are called **lateral faces**.

The altitude or   height   of each   lateral face   is called the **slant height**.

The sum of the   areas   of the   lateral faces   is the **lateral area**.

EXAMPLE   Surface Area of a Pyramid

1 Find the surface area of the triangular pyramid.

Find the lateral area and the area of the base.

Area of each lateral face

$A = \boxed{\frac{1}{2}bh}$ Area of a triangle

$A = \frac{1}{2}(\boxed{5})(\boxed{8})$ or $\boxed{20}$ Replace b with $\boxed{5}$ and h with $\boxed{8}$.

There are 3 faces, so the lateral area is $3(\boxed{20})$ or $\boxed{60}$ square inches.

Area of base

$A = \boxed{10.8 \text{ in}^2}$

The surface area of the pyramid is $\boxed{60} + \boxed{10.8}$ or $\boxed{70.8}$ square inches.

FOLDABLES

ORGANIZE IT

On a card, write the formula for finding the surface area of a pyramid. Then sketch a pyramid and label the parts. Place the card in the "Area" pocket of your Foldable.

© Glencoe/McGraw-Hill

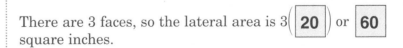

Mathematics: Applications and Concepts, Course 3   **183**

Your Turn Find the surface area of the square pyramid.

156 cm²

10 cm

6 cm

EXAMPLE Surface Area of a Cone

KEY CONCEPT

Surface Area of a Cone
The surface area S of a cone with slant height ℓ and radius r is the lateral area plus the area of the base.

2 **Find the surface of the cone. Round to the nearest tenth.**

4.5 m

1.5 m

$S = \pi r\ell +$ $\boxed{\pi r^2}$ Surface area of a cone

$S = \pi\left(\boxed{1.5}\right)\left(\boxed{4.5}\right) = \pi\left(\boxed{1.5}\right)^2$ $r = \boxed{1.5}$, $\ell = \boxed{4.5}$

$S \approx \boxed{28.3}$ Simplify.

The surface area of the cone is about $\boxed{28.3}$ square meters.

Your Turn Find the surface area of the cone. Round to the nearest tenth.

108.4 cm²

8.5 cm

3 cm

HOMEWORK ASSIGNMENT

Page(s):

Exercises:

Precision and Significant Digits

BUILD YOUR VOCABULARY (pages 164–165)

The **precision** of a measurement is the [**exactness**] to which a measurement is made.

Significant digits are all of the digits of a measurement that are known to be [**accurate**] plus one [**estimated**] digit.

WHAT YOU'LL LEARN
• Analyze measurements.

EXAMPLE Identify Precision Units

① **Identify the precision unit of the thermometer.**

There are [**5**] spaces between each

10° mark, so the precision unit is [$\frac{1}{5}$]

of 10 degrees or [**2**] degrees.

Fahrenheit

REMEMBER IT 💡

The precision unit of a measuring instrument determines the number of significant digits.

Your Turn Identify the precision unit of the ruler.

$\frac{1}{4}$ inch

EXAMPLES Identify Significant Digits

Determine the number of significant digits in each measure.

2 5,000 ft

   1 significant digit

3 315.05 ounces

   5 significant digits

Your Turn Determine the number of significant digits in each measure.

a. 21.0 miles

b. 35.006 centimeters

3 significant digits

5 significant digits

EXAMPLE Add Measurements

4 MAIL Venita took four packages to the post office. They weighed 1.27 pounds, 3.45 pounds, 0.524 pound, and 2.7 pounds. Write the combined weight of her mail using correct precision.

1.27 ⟵ **2** decimal places

3.45 ⟵ **2** decimal places

0.524 ⟵ **3** decimal places

+2.7 ⟵ 1 decimal place ⟵ The least precise measurement has 1 decimal place, so round the sum to 1 decimal place.

7.944

The combined weight of the packages is about **7.9** pounds.

Your Turn Veric bought 1.5 pounds of turkey, 0.75 pound of roast beef, 2.4 pounds of ham, and 0.5 pound of salami. Write the combined weight of the lunch meat that Veric bought using correct precision.

5.2 lb

EXAMPLE Multiply Measurements

5 Use the correct number of significant digits to find the volume of the cylinder. Use 3.14 for pi.

4.125 in.

3.5 in.

$V = \pi r^2 h$

Volume of a cylinder

$V = (3.14)(\boxed{4.125})^2(\boxed{3.5})$

The height of the cylinder has the least number of significant digits, 2.

$V = 187.0017188$

Round the answer, 187.0017188, so that it has **2**

significant digits. The volume of the cylinder is about **190** cubic inches.

Your Turn Use the correct number of significant digits to find the volume of the rectangular prism.

82 in³

4.3 in.
3.65 in.
5.21 in.

REVIEW IT
What is the formula for finding the volume of a rectangular prism? *(Lesson 7-5)*

HOMEWORK ASSIGNMENT
Page(s):
Exercises:

FOLDABLES™	VOCABULARY PUZZLEMAKER	**BUILD YOUR VOCABULARY**
Use your **Chapter 7 Foldable** to help you study for your chapter test.	To make a crossword puzzle, word search, or jumble puzzle of the vocabulary words in Chapter 7, go to: www.glencoe.com/sec/math/ t_resources/free/index.php	You can use your completed **Vocabulary Builder** *(pages 164–165)* to help you solve the puzzle.

7-1

Area of Parallelograms, Triangles, and Trapezoids

Find the area of each figure.

1. triangle: base, 14 m; height, 4 m

   28 m²

2. parallelogram: base, 5 ft; height, 9.2 ft

   46 ft²

3. trapezoid: bases, 2 in. and 6 in.; height, 4.3 in.

   17.2 in²

4. trapezoid: bases, 3 yd and 12 yd; height 10 yd

   75 yd²

7-2

Circumference and Area of Circles

Complete.

5. The distance from the center of a circle to any point on the

   circle is called the ⬚ **radius** , while the distance around the

   circle is called the ⬚ **circumference** .

Find the circumference and area of each circle. Round to the nearest tenth.

6. The radius is 14 miles.

   C = 88 mi; A = 615.8 mi²

7. The diameter is 17.4 in².

   C = 54.7 in.; A = 237.8 in²

7-3

Area of Complex Figures

8. What is a complex figure?

> **Sample answer: a figure made up of two or more shapes**

9. What is the first step in finding the area of a complex figure?

> **Sample answer: Separate the figure into shapes whose areas you know how to find.**

10. Explain how to divide up the figure shown.

> **Sample answer: Draw a vertical line separating a triangle on the right. Draw two additional vertical lines in the left part, forming three rectangles.**

7-4

Three-Dimensional Figures

Match each description with the word it describes.

11. a flat surface c

12. a polyhedron with one base that is a polygon and faces that are triangles f

13. where three or more planes intersect at a point a

14. where two planes intersect in a line b

15. a polyhedron with two parallel, congruent faces e

- **a.** vertex
- **b.** edge
- **c.** face
- **d.** base
- **e.** prism
- **f.** pyramid

7-5

Volume of Prisms and Cylinders

Find the volume of each solid. Round to the nearest tenth if necessary.

16.

31.2 m

15.1 m   10.0 m

| **4,711.2 m³** |

17.

5 cm

9 cm

| **706.9 cm³** |

18.

14 mm

12.1 mm

37 mm

14 mm

| **3,133.9 mm³** |

7-6

Volume of Pyramids and Cones

19. Fill in the table about what you know from the diagram. Then complete the volume of the pyramid.

11 in.

6 in.

8 in.

length of rectangle	**11 in.**
width of rectangle	**6 in.**
area of base	**48 in²**
height of pyramid	**11 in.**
volume of pyramid	**176 in³**

7-7

Surface Area of Prisms and Cylinders

20. Complete the sentence with the correct numbers. When you draw a net of a triangular prism, there are **2** congruent triangular faces and **3** rectangular faces.

21. If you unroll a cylinder, what does the net look like?

| **2 circles and a rectangle** |

22. Find the surface area of the cylinder. Round the nearest tenth.

| **1,319.5 cm²** |

20 cm

11 cm

7-8
Surface Area of Pyramids and Cones

23. Complete the steps in finding the surface area of a pyramid.
Area of each lateral face

$A = \frac{1}{2}bh$ | **Area of a triangle**

$A = \frac{1}{2}(9)(16)$ | **Replace *b* with 9 and *h* with 16.**

$A = 72$ | **Simplify.**

There are $\boxed{4}$ faces, so the lateral area is $4(72) = \boxed{288}$ square inches.

Area of base

$A = s^2$ | **Area of a square**

$A = 9^2$ or 81 | **Replace *s* with 9.**

The surface area of the pyramid is $\boxed{288} + \boxed{81}$ or

$\boxed{369}$ square inches.

24. What two areas are needed to calculate the surface area of a cone?

Sample answer: area of its base and area of its curved side

7-9
Precision and Significant Digits

25. How do you determine that a measurement is accurate?

Sample answer: when it is measured to the nearest precision unit

26. What determines the number of significant digits?

Sample answer: the precision unit of a measuring instrument

ARE YOU READY FOR THE CHAPTER TEST?

Math Online

Visit **msmath3.net** to access your textbook, more examples, self-check quizzes, and practice tests to help you study the concepts in Chapter 7.

Check the one that applies. Suggestions to help you study are given with each item.

☐ **I completed the review of all or most lessons without using my notes or asking for help.**

- You are probably ready for the Chapter Test.
- You may want to take the Chapter 7 Practice Test on page 367 of your textbook as a final check.

☐ **I used my Foldable or Study Notebook to complete the review of all or most lessons.**

- You should complete the Chapter 7 Study Guide and Review on pages 363–366 of your textbook.
- If you are unsure of any concepts or skills, refer to the specific lesson(s).
- You may also want to take the Chapter 7 Practice Test on page 367.

☐ **I asked for help from someone else to complete the review of all or most lessons.**

- You should review the examples and concepts in your Study Notebook and Chapter 7 Foldable.
- Then complete the Chapter 7 Study Guide and Review on pages 363–366 of your textbook.
- If you are unsure of any concepts or skills, refer to the specific lesson(s).
- You may also want to take the Chapter 7 Practice Test on page 367.

Student Signature

Parent/Guardian Signature

Teacher Signature

Probabilty

Use the instructions below to make a Foldable to help you organize your notes as you study the chapter. You will see Foldable reminders in the margin of this Interactive Study Notebook to help you in taking notes.

Begin with two sheets of 8.5" × 11" unlined paper.

STEP 1 **Fold in Quarters**
Fold each sheet in quarters along the width.

STEP 2 **Tape**
Unfold each sheet and tape to form one long piece.

STEP 3 **Label**
Label each page with the lesson number to form one long piece.

 NOTE-TAKING TIP: It helps to take notes as you progress through studying a subject. New concepts often build upon concepts you have just learned in a previous lesson. If you take notes as you go, you will know what you need to know for the concept you are now learning.

BUILD YOUR VOCABULARY

This is an alphabetical list of new vocabulary terms you will learn in Chapter 8. As you complete the study notes for the chapter, you will see Build Your Vocabulary reminders to complete each term's definition or description on these pages. Remember to add the textbook page number in the second column for reference when you study.

Vocabulary Term	Found on Page	Definition	Description or Example
biased sample			
combination			
complementary events			
compound events			
dependent events			
experimental probability			
factorial			
Fundamental Counting Principle			
independent events			
outcome			

Vocabulary Term	Found on Page	Definition	Description or Example
permutation			
population			
probability			
random			
sample			
stratified random sample			
systematic random sample			
theoretical probability			
tree diagram			
unbiased sample			

Probability of Simple Events

WHAT YOU'LL LEARN

- Find the probability of a simple event.

KEY CONCEPT

Probability The probability of an event is a ratio that compares the number of favorable outcomes to the number of possible outcomes.

BUILD YOUR VOCABULARY (pages 194–195)

An **outcome** is one possible ┃ result ┃ of a probability event.

If all outcomes occur by chance the outcomes happen at **random**.

Probability is the ┃ chance ┃ that an event will happen.

EXAMPLES Find Probabilities

A bag contains 5 blue marbles, 10 red marbles, and 10 yellow marbles. A marble is picked at random.

① What is the probability the marble is yellow?

There are 5 + 10 + 10 or 25 marbles in the bag.

$$P(\text{yellow}) = \frac{\boxed{\text{yellow}} \text{ marbles}}{\boxed{\text{total}} \text{ number of marbles}}$$

$$= \boxed{\frac{10}{25}} \text{ or } \boxed{\frac{2}{5}}$$

There are ┃ 10 ┃ yellow marbles

out of ┃ 25 ┃ marbles.

The probability the marble is yellow is ┃ $\frac{2}{5}$ **0.4, or 40%** ┃.

② What is the probability the marble is blue or red?

$$P(\text{blue or red}) = \frac{\boxed{\text{blue}} \text{ marbles} + \boxed{\text{red}} \text{ marbles}}{\text{total number of marbles}}$$

$$= \frac{5 + 10}{25}$$

There are 5 blue marbles and 10 red marbles.

$$= \boxed{\frac{15}{25}} \text{ or } \boxed{\frac{3}{5}}$$

Simplify.

The probability the marble is blue or red is ┃ $\frac{3}{5}$ **0.6 or 60%** ┃.

Your Turn A bag contains 3 green marbles, 7 purple marbles, and 15 black marbles. A marble is picked at random.

a. What is the probability the marble is black?

$$\frac{3}{5}$$

b. What is the probability the marble is green or purple?

$$\frac{2}{5}$$

c. What is the probability the marble is red?

0

ORGANIZE IT

Under Lesson 8-1, explain how to find probabilities. Include examples and diagrams. On the last page in your Foldable, write the key terms in the lesson and their definitions.

BUILD YOUR VOCABULARY (page 194)

The events of one outcome happening and that outcome **not** happenning are **complementary events**.

EXAMPLE Probability of a Complementary Event
(parallels Example 4 in text)

3 PHONE LISTINGS One town has 10,000 phone numbers in use. Of these, 500 are not listed in the local phone book. What is the probability that the pone number you are looking for is listed in the phone book?

| 10,000 | – | 500 | or | 9,500 | phone numbers are listed.

$$P(\text{listed}) = \frac{\text{listed numbers}}{\text{total number of phone numbers}}$$ Definition of probability

$$= \frac{9,500}{10,000} \text{ or } \frac{19}{20}$$ There are 9,500 listed phone numbers.

The probability is $\frac{19}{20}$.

HOMEWORK ASSIGNMENT

Page(s):

Exercises:

Your Turn Oakdale Junior High School has a total enrollment of 670 students. Of these, 45 are absent today. Suppose a student's name is picked at random. What is the probability that the student picked is absent today?

$$\frac{9}{134}$$

Counting Outcomes

WHAT YOU'LL LEARN

• Count outcomes by using a tree diagram or the Fundamental Counting Principle.

BUILD YOUR VOCABULARY (pages 194–195)

A **tree diagram** is a diagram used to show the **total** number of **possible outcomes** in a probability experiment.

The **Fundamental Counting Principle** uses **multiplication** of the number of ways each event in an experiment can occur to find the number of **possible outcomes** in a sample space.

EXAMPLE Use a Tree Diagram

WRITE IT

How is using a tree diagram to find total number of outcomes like using a factor tree to find prime factors? (see factor trees in Prerequisite Skills page 609)

_____

_____

_____

_____

1 BOOKS A flea market vendor sells new and used books for adults and teens. Today she has fantasy novels and poetry collections to choose from. Draw a tree diagram to determine the number of categories of books.

| List new or used book. | Each type is paired with new or used. | Each age group is paired with each type and new/used. | List all of the outcomes of book categories. |

| New/Used | Type | Age Group | Outcome |

		Adult ——	New, Fantasy Novel, Adult
	Fantasy novels	Teen ——	New, Fantasy Novel, Teen
New		Adult ——	New, Poetry, Adult
	Poetry	Teen ——	New, Poetry, Teen
		Adult ——	Used, Fantasy Novel, Adult
	Fantasy novels	Teen ——	Used, Fantasy Novel, Teen
Used		Adult ——	Used, Poetry, Adult
	Poetry	Teen ——	Used, Poetry, Teen

There are $\boxed{8}$ different categories.

KEY CONCEPT

Fundamental Counting Principle If event *M* an occur in *m* ways and is followed by event *N* that can occur in n ways, then the event *M* followed by the event *N* can occur in $m \cdot n$ ways.

Your Turn A store has spring outfits on sale. You can choose either striped or solid pants. You can also choose green, pink, or orange shirts. Finally, you can choose either long-sleeved shirts or short-sleeved shirts. Draw a tree diagram to determine the number of possible outfits.

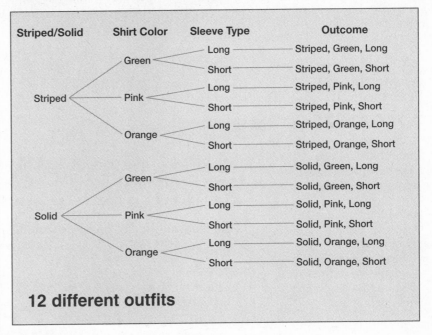

12 different outfits

EXAMPLE Use the Fundamental Counting Principle

2 **RESTAURANTS** A manager assigns different codes to all the tables in a restaurant to make it easier for the wait staff to identify them. Each code consists of the vowel A, E, I, O, or U, followed by two digits from 0 through 9. How many codes could the manager assign using this method?

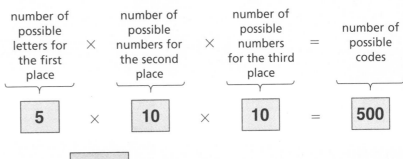

There are [500] possible codes.

ORGANIZE IT

Under Lesson 8-2, write notes on what you learned about counting outcomes by using a tree diagram and by using the Counting Principle. Include examples of each. On the last page of your Foldable, write the key terms in the lesson and their definitions.

Your Turn A middle school assigns each student a code to use for scheduling. Each code consists of a letter, followed by two digits from 0 though 9. How many codes are possible?

2,600

EXAMPLE Find Probability

3 **COMPUTERS** **What is the probability that Liana will guess her friend's computer password on the first try if all she knows is that it consists of three letters?**

Find the number of possible outcomes. Use the Fundamental Counting Principle.

choices for the first letter	×	choices the second letter	×	choices for the third letter	=	total number of outcomes
26	×	26	×	26	=	17,576

There are 17,576 possible outcomes. There is 1

correct password. So, the probability of guessing on the first

try is $\dfrac{1}{17{,}576}$.

Your Turn What is the probability that Shauna will guess her friend's locker combination on the first try if all she knows is that it consists of three digits from 0 through 9?

$\dfrac{1}{1{,}000}$

HOMEWORK ASSIGNMENT

Page(s): _____

Exercises: _____

WHAT YOU'LL LEARN

- Find the number of permutations of objects.

BUILD YOUR VOCABULARY (pages 194–195)

A **permutation** is an arrangement or listing in which

order is important .

A **factorial** is a mathematical expression in which $n!$ is the

product of all counting numbers beginning

with n and counting backward to 1 .

EXAMPLE Find a Permutation

1 **SOFTBALL** There are 10 players on a softball team. In how many ways can the manager choose three players for first, second, and third base?

number of possible players for first base	×	number of possible players for second base	×	number of possible players for third base	=	total number of possible ways
10	×	9	×	8	=	720

There are 720 different ways the manager can pick players for first, second, and third base.

Your Turn There are 15 students on student council. In how many ways can Mrs. Sommers choose three students for president, vice president, and secretary?

2,730

FOLDABLES

ORGANIZE IT

Under Lesson 8-3, explain how to find the number of permutations of objects. Use words and symbols and include examples.

EXAMPLE Use Permutation Notation

2 Find each value.

$P(7, 2)$

$P(7, 2) =$ 7 · 6 or 42   7 things taken 2 at a time.

Mathematics: Applications and Concepts, Course 3 **201**

Your Turn Find each value.

a. $P(8, 4)$

1,680

b. $P(12, 5)$

95,040

EXAMPLE Find Probability (parallels Example 4 in text)

3 Consider all of the five-digit numbers that can be formed using the digits 1, 2, 3, 4, and 5 where no digit is used twice. Find the probability that one of these numbers picked at random is an even number.

Find the number of possible five-digit numbers.

$P(5, 5) = \boxed{5}\,!$

In order for a number to be even, the ones digit must be 2 or 4.

number of ways to pick the last digit	$\times$	number of ways to pick the first four digits	$=$	number of permutations that are even
$\boxed{2}$	$\times$	$P\,\boxed{(4, 4)}$	$=$	$2P(4, 4)$ or $\boxed{2 \times 4}\,!$

$$P(\text{even}) = \frac{\text{number of permutations that are even}}{\text{total number of permutations}}$$

$$= \boxed{\frac{2 \times 4!}{5!}} \qquad \text{Substitute.}$$

$$= \frac{2 \cdot \overset{1}{4} \cdot \overset{1}{3} \cdot \overset{1}{2} \cdot \overset{1}{1}}{5 \cdot \underset{1}{4} \cdot \underset{1}{3} \cdot \underset{1}{2} \cdot \underset{1}{1}} \qquad \text{Definition of factorial}$$

$$= \boxed{\frac{2}{5}} \text{ or } \boxed{40\%} \qquad \text{Simplify.}$$

The probability is $\boxed{40\%}$.

Your Turn Consider all of the five-digit numbers that can be formed using the digits 1, 2, 3, 4, and 5 where no digit is used twice. Find the probability that one of these numbers picked at random is an odd number.

60%

Combinations

WHAT YOU'LL LEARN

• Find the number of combinations of objects.

BUILD YOUR VOCABULARY (page 194)

A **combination** is an arrangement or listing in which

| order is not important |.

EXAMPLE Find a Combination

1 TOURNAMENTS Five teams are playing each other in a tournament. If each team plays every other team once, how many games are played?

Method 1

Let A, B, C, D, and E represent the five teams. First, list all of

the possible permutations of A, B, C, D, and E taken | **two** |

at a time. Then cross out the letter pairs that are the same as one another.

AB	AC	AD	AE	$\cancel{BA}$
BC	BD	BE	$\cancel{CA}$	$\cancel{CB}$
CD	CE	$\cancel{DA}$	$\cancel{DB}$	$\cancel{DC}$
DE	$\cancel{EA}$	$\cancel{EB}$	$\cancel{EC}$	$\cancel{ED}$

Team A playing Team B is the same as Team B playing Team A, so cross off one of them.

There are only | **10** | different games

Method 2

Find the number of permutations of 5 teams taken | **2** | at a time.

$P(5, 2) = 5 \cdot 4$ or | **20** |

Since order is not important, divide the number of permutations by the number of ways 2 things can be arranged.

$$\frac{20}{2!} = \frac{20}{\boxed{2} \cdot \boxed{1}} \text{ or } \boxed{10}$$

There are | **10** | games that can be played.

Your Turn Six teams are playing each other in a tournament. If each team plays every other tream once, how many games are played?

> **15**

EXAMPLE Use Combination Notation

② Find $C(8, 5)$.

$C(8, 5) = \dfrac{P(8, 5)}{\boxed{5!}}$ Definition of $C(8, 5)$

$= \dfrac{8 \cdot 7 \cdot \overset{1}{\underset{1}{\cancel{6}}} \cdot \overset{1}{\underset{1}{\cancel{5}}} \cdot \overset{1}{\underset{1}{\cancel{4}}}}{\underset{1}{\cancel{5}} \cdot \underset{1}{\cancel{4}} \cdot \underset{1}{\cancel{3}} \cdot \underset{1}{\cancel{2}} \cdot 1}$ or $\boxed{56}$ $P(8, 5) = \boxed{8 \cdot 7 \cdot 6 \cdot 5 \cdot 4}$

                   and $5! = \boxed{5 \cdot 4 \cdot 3 \cdot 2 \cdot 1}$

Your Turn Find $C(6, 3)$.

> **20**

EXAMPLES Combinations and Permutations

SCHOOL An eighth grade teacher needs to select 4 students from a class of 22 to help with sixth grade orientation.

③ Does this represent a combination or a permutation? How many possible groups could be selected to help out the new students?

This is a $\boxed{\textbf{combination}}$ problem since the order is not important.

$C(22, 4) = \dfrac{P(22, 4)}{4!}$ 22 students taken 4 at a time.

$= \dfrac{\overset{11}{\cancel{22}} \cdot \overset{7}{\cancel{21}} \cdot \overset{5}{\cancel{20}} \cdot 19}{\underset{1}{\cancel{4}} \cdot \underset{1}{\cancel{3}} \cdot \underset{1}{\cancel{2}} \cdot 1}$ or $\boxed{7,315}$

There are $\boxed{7,315}$ different groups of eighth grade students that could help the new students.

REVIEW IT

Explain the difference between combinations and *permutations*. (Lesson 8-3)

_____

_____

_____

_____

_____

_____

© Glencoe/McGraw-Hill

④ SCHOOL One eighth grade student will be assigned to sixth grade classes on the first floor, another student will be assigned to classes on the second floor, another student will be assigned to classes on the third floor, and still another student will be assigned to classes on the fourth floor. Does this represent a combination or a permutation? In how many possible ways can the eighth graders be assigned to help with the sixth grade orientation?

Since it makes a difference which student goes to which floor, order is important. This is a **permutation**.

$P(22, 4) = 22 \cdot 21 \cdot 20 \cdot \boxed{19}$ Definition of $P(22, 4)$

$= 175{,}560$

There are **175,560 ways** for the eighth grade students to be selected to help with sixth grade orientation.

Your Turn A teacher needs to select 5 students from a class of 26 to help with parent teacher conferences.

a. Does this represent a combination or a permutation? How many possible groups could be selected to help?

combination; 65,780

b. One student will be assigned to fifth grade parents, another student will be assigned to sixth grade parents, another student will be assigned to seventh grade parents, another student will be assigned to ninth grade parents. Does this represent a combination or a permutation? In how many possible ways can the students be assigned to help with the parent teacher conferences?

permutation; 7,893,600

FOLDABLES™

ORGANIZE IT

Under Lesson 8-4, write notes on what you learned about finding the number of combinations of objects. Include examples. On the last page in your Foldable, write the key terms in the lesson and their definitions.

HOMEWORK ASSIGNMENT

Page(s): _____

Exercises: _____

_____

Probability of Compound Events

WHAT YOU'LL LEARN

• Find the probability of independent and dependent events.

BUILD YOUR VOCABULARY (page 194)

A **compound event** consists of ⟨two or more⟩ simple events.

Independent events are ⟨two or more⟩ events in which the outcome of one event ⟨does not⟩ affect the outcome of the other events.

KEY CONCEPT

Probability of Two Independent Events The probability of two independent events can be found by multiplying the probability of the first event by the probability of the second event.

EXAMPLE Probability of Independent Events

1 The two spinners below are spun. What is the probability that both spinners will show a number greater than 6?

P(first spinner is greater than 6) = $\dfrac{3}{10}$

P(second spinner is greater than 6) = $\dfrac{3}{10}$

P(both spinners are greater than 6) = $\dfrac{3}{10} \cdot \dfrac{3}{10}$ or $\dfrac{9}{100}$

Your Turn The two spinners below are spun. What is the probability that both spinners will show a number less than 4?

$\dfrac{3}{16}$

EXAMPLE Use a Probability to Solve a Problem

2 **POPULATION** Use the information below. What is the probability that a student picked at random will be an eighth-grade girl?

$P(\text{8th grade}) = \boxed{\dfrac{3}{10}}$

$P(\text{girl}) = \boxed{\dfrac{5}{9}}$

$P(\text{8th grade and girl}) =$

$\dfrac{3}{\overset{10}{\underset{2}{\cancel{10}}}} \cdot \dfrac{5}{\overset{9}{\underset{3}{\cancel{9}}}}$ or $\boxed{\dfrac{1}{6}}$

Cross River Middle School	
Demographic Group	**Fraction of the Population**
Grade 6	$\dfrac{4}{10}$
Grade 7	$\dfrac{3}{10}$
Grade 8	$\dfrac{3}{10}$
Boys	$\dfrac{4}{9}$
Girls	$\dfrac{5}{9}$

The probability that the $\boxed{\textbf{two}}$ events will occur is $\frac{1}{6}$.

Your Turn Use the information in the table. What is the probability that a student picked at random will be a sixth grade boy?

$\dfrac{7}{45}$

Monterey Middle School	
Demographic Group	**Fraction of the Population**
Grade 6	$\dfrac{2}{9}$
Grade 7	$\dfrac{4}{9}$
Grade 8	$\dfrac{1}{3}$
Boys	$\dfrac{7}{10}$
Girls	$\dfrac{3}{10}$

KEY CONCEPT

Probability of Two Dependent Events If two events, *A* and *B*, are dependent, then the probability of both events occurring is the product of the probability of *A* and the probability of *B* after *A* occurs.

BUILD YOUR VOCABULARY (page 194)

If the outcome of one event does $\boxed{\textbf{affect}}$ the outcome of another event, the compound events are called **dependent events**.

EXAMPLE Probability of Dependent Events

3 There are 4 red, 8 yellow, and 6 blue socks in a drawer. Once a sock is selected, it is not replaced. Find the probability that two blue socks are chosen.

Since the first sock $\boxed{\textbf{is not}}$ replaced, the first event affects the second event. These are dependent events.

$P(\text{first sock is blue}) = \boxed{\dfrac{6}{18}}$ ⟵ number of blue socks
⟵ total number of socks

$P(\text{second sock is blue}) = \boxed{\dfrac{5}{17}}$ ⟵ {number of blue socks after one blue sock is removed

⟵ {total number of socks after one blue sock is removed

$P(\text{two blue socks}) = \boxed{\dfrac{\overset{1}{6}}{\underset{3}{18}} \cdot \dfrac{5}{17}}$ or $\boxed{\dfrac{5}{51}}$

Your Turn There are 6 green, 9 purple, and 3 orange marbles in a bag. Once a marble is selected, it is not replaced. Find the probability that two purple marbles are chosen.

$\dfrac{4}{17}$

Experimental Probability

© Glencoe/McGraw-Hill

WHAT YOU'LL LEARN

• Find experimental probability.

BUILD YOUR VOCABULARY (pages 194–195)

A probability that is based on **frequencies** obtained

by conducting an **experiment** is called an

experimental probability.

A probabililty that is based on **known characteristics**

or facts is called a **theoretical probability**.

EXAMPLES Experimental Probability

Nikki is conducting an experiment to find the probability of getting various results when three coins are tossed. The results of her experiment are given in the table.

Result	Number of Tosses
all heads	6
two heads	32
one head	30
no heads	12

1 According to the experimental probability, is Nikki more likely to get all heads or no heads on the next toss?

Based on the results so far, **no** heads is more likely.

2 How many possible outcomes are there for tossing three coins if order is important?

There are 2 · 2 · 2 or **8** possible outcomes.

Your Turn Marcus is conducting an experiment to find the probability of getting various results when four coins are tossed. The results of his experiment are given in the table.

Result	Number of Tosses
all heads	6
three heads	12
two heads	20
one head	7
no heads	5

a. According to the experiment probability, is Marcus more likely to get all heads or no heads on the next toss?

> **all heads**

b. How many possible outcomes are there for tossing four coins if order is important?

> **16**

EXAMPLE Theoretical Probability

❸ Nikki is conducting an experiment to find the probability of getting various results when three coins are tossed. The results of her experiment are given in the table below. Is the theoretical probability greater for tossing all heads or no heads? What is the theoretical probability of each?

Result	Number of Tosses
all heads	6
two heads	32
one head	30
no heads	12

The theoretical probability of **all** heads is

$$\frac{1}{2} \cdot \frac{1}{2} \cdot \frac{1}{2} \text{ or } \frac{1}{8}.$$

The theoretical probability of **no** heads is

$$\frac{1}{2} \cdot \frac{1}{2} \cdot \frac{1}{2} \text{ or } \frac{1}{8}.$$

The theoretical probabilities are **the same** .

Your Turn Marcus is conducting an experiment to find the probability of getting various results when four coins are tossed. The results of his experiment are given below. Is the theoretical probability greater for tossing all heads or no heads? What is the theoretical probability of each?

Result	Number of Tosses
all heads	6
three heads	12
two heads	20
one head	7
no heads	5

same; $\frac{1}{16}$

FOLDABLES

ORGANIZE IT

Under Lesson 8-6, write a few words to compare and contrast experimental and theoretical probabilities. On the last page in your Foldable, write the key terms in the lesson and their definitions.

EXAMPLE Experimental Probability

4 **MARKETING** **Eight hundred adults were asked whether they were planning to stay home for winter vacation. Of those surveyed, 560 said that they were. What is the experimental probability that an adult planned to stay home for winter vacation?**

There were **800** people surveyed and **560** said that they were staying home.

The experimental probability is $\frac{560}{800}$ or $\frac{7}{10}$.

Your Turn Five hundred adults were asked whether they were planning to stay home for New Year's Eve. Of those surveyed, 300 said that they were. What is the experimental probability that an adult planned to stay home for New Year's Eve?

$\frac{3}{5}$

EXAMPLES Use Probability to Predict

MATH TEAM Over the past three years, the probability that the school math team would win a meet is $\frac{3}{5}$.

5 Is this probability experimental or theoretical? Explain.

This is an experimental probability since it is based on what

happened in the [**past**].

REVIEW IT

Explain what a proportion is and how you can solve a proportion. *(Lesson 4-4)*

_____

_____

_____

_____

_____

_____

6 If the team wants to win 12 more meets in the next 3 years, how many meets should the team enter?

This problem can be solved using a proportion.

| 3 out of 5 meets were wins | → $\frac{3}{5} = \frac{12}{x}$ ← | 12 out of x meets should be wins. |

Solve the proportion.

$$\frac{3}{5} = \frac{12}{x}$$ Write the proportion.

$3 \cdot x = 5 \cdot 12$ Find the cross products.

$3x = 60$ Multiply.

$\frac{3x}{3} = \frac{60}{3}$ Divide each side by [3].

$x = $ [20]

They should enter [20] meets.

Your Turn Over the past three years, the probability that the school speech and debate team would win a meet is $\frac{4}{5}$.

a. Is this probability experimental or theoretical? Explain.

Experimental; it is based on actual results.

b. If the team wants to win 20 more meets in the next 3 years, how many meets should the team enter?

25 meets

Using Sampling to Predict

BUILD YOUR VOCABULARY (pages 194–195)

A **sample** is a | randomly | selected group chosen for the purpose of collecting data.

The **population** is the | entire group | from which the samples under consideration are taken.

An **unbiased sample** is selected so that it is

| representative | of the entire population.

In a **stratified random sample**, the population is divided

into | similar |, nonoverlapping groups.

In a **systematic random sample**, the items or people are

selected according to a specific | time | or item interval.

In a **biased sample**, one or more parts of the population

are | favored | over others.

EXAMPLES Describe Samples

Describe each sample.

❶ **To determine which school lunches students like most, every twentieth student to walk into the cafeteria is surveyed.**

Since the population is the students entering the cafeteria,

the sample is a | systematic random sample |. It is an

| unbiased | sample.

2 To determine what sports teenagers like, the student athletes on the girls' field hockey team are surveyed.

Teenagers on the field hockey team are more likely to choose field hockey. This is a ┃ **biased** ┃ sample. The sample is a

┃ **convenience** ┃ sample because the people are easily accessed.

Your Turn Describe each sample.

a. To determine which CDs customers like most, every tenth customer to walk into the music store is surveyed.

> **This is an unbiased, systematic random sample.**

b. To determine what restaurant teenagers like, the teenagers eating at Pete's Diner are surveyed.

> **This is a biased convenience sample.**

EXAMPLES Using Sampling to Predict

BOOKS The student council is trying to decide what types of books to sell at its annual book fair to help raise money for the eighth-grade trip. It surveys 40 students at random. The books they prefer are in the table.

3 What percent of the students prefer mysteries?

┃ **12** ┃ out of ┃ **40** ┃ students prefer mysteries.

┃ **12** ┃ ÷ ┃ **40** ┃ = ┃ **0.30** ┃

So, ┃ **30%** ┃ of the students prefer mysteries.

4 **If 220 books are to be sold at the book fair, how many should be mysteries?**

Find 30% of 220 .

$0.30 \times$ 220 $=$ 66

About 66 books should be mysteries.

ORGANIZE IT

Under Lesson 8-7, list the different types of samples and how to use them to make predictions. Give examples. On the last page of your Foldable, write the key terms in the lesson and their definitions.

Your Turn **The student shop sells pens. It surveys 50 students at random. The pens they prefer are in the table.**

Type	Number
gel pens	22
ball point	8
glitter pens	10
roller balls	10

a. What percent of the students prefer gel pens?

44%

b. If 300 pens are to be sold at the student shop, how many should be gel pens?

132

HOMEWORK ASSIGNMENT

Page(s):

Exercises:

BRINGING IT ALL TOGETHER

STUDY GUIDE

FOLDABLES™	VOCABULARY PUZZLEMAKER	*BUILD YOUR VOCABULARY*
Use your **Chapter 8 Foldable** to help you study for your chapter test.	To make a crossword puzzle, word search, or jumble puzzle of the vocabulary words in Chapter 8, go to: www.glencoe.com/sec/math/t_resources/free/index.php	You can use your completed **Vocabulary Builder** *(pages 194–195)* to help you solve the puzzle.

8-1

Probability of Simple Events

1. Complete the sentence. Probability is a ratio that compares the

number of $\boxed{\textbf{favorable}}$ outcomes to the number of

$\boxed{\textbf{possible}}$ outcomes.

A spinner is divided into 8 equal parts, and one of the first eight letters of the alphabet is placed in each section such that all the letters are used.

2. What is the sample space?

$\boxed{\textbf{A, B, C, D, E, F, G, H}}$

3. What is the probability of spinning a vowel? $\boxed{\dfrac{1}{8} \textbf{ or 12.5\%}}$

4. If an event has a probability of 0.1, what does this mean?

$\boxed{\textbf{Sample answer: The event is not likely to occur or has a very small chance of occurring.}}$

5. If you are given the probability of an event happening, how can you find the probability of the event *not* happening?

$\boxed{\textbf{Sample answer: Subtract the probability of the event happening from one.}}$

Counting Outcomes

6. Complete the tree diagram shown below for how many boys and and how many girls are likely to be in a family of three children.

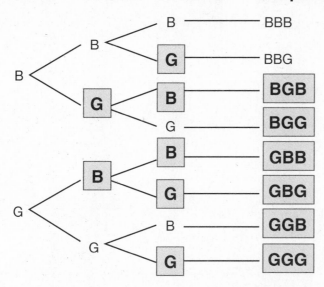

| Child 1 | Child 2 | Child 3 | Sample Outcome |

7. Use the Fundamental Counting Principle to find the number of possible outcomes if there are 4 true-false questions on a test.

$$2 \times 2 \times 2 \times 2 = 16$$

Permutations

8. What does the notation $P(14, 4)$ represent?

> **the number of permutations of 14 things taken 4 at a time**

9. What is the difference between $6!$ and $P(6, 4)$?

> $6! = 6 \cdot 5 \cdot 4 \cdot 3 \cdot 2 \cdot 1$ and $P(6, 4) = 6 \cdot 5 \cdot 4$

A security system has a number pad with 9 digits.

10. How many three-number passwords are available if a digit cannot be repeated?

> 504

11. If a digit can be repeated, how many passwords are available?

> 729

8-4

Combinations

12. What is the difference between a permutation and a combination?

> **For a combination, order is not important; whereas, for a permutation, order is important.**

13. Fill in the blanks to find $C(9, 4)$.

$$C(9, 4) = \frac{P(9, 4)}{\boxed{4}!}$$

$$= \frac{9 \cdot \boxed{8} \cdot \boxed{7} \cdot \boxed{6}}{4 \cdot \boxed{3} \cdot \boxed{2} \cdot \boxed{1}} \quad \text{or} \quad \boxed{126}$$

14. Are there more combinations or permutations of 3 people chosen from a group of 6 people? Explain.

> **Sample answer: There are more permutations. You divide the number of permutations by the number of ways the items cam be arranged to find the number of combinations.**

8-5

Probability of Compound Events

15. What is a compound event?

> **an event consisting of two or more simple events**

16. Are the events of spinning a spinner and rolling a number cube independent events? Why or why not?

> **Sample answer: Yes; the outcome of spinning the spinner does not affect the event of rolling a number cube.**

A number cube is rolled and a penny is tossed. Find each probability.

17. $P(4 \text{ and tails})$

> $\dfrac{1}{12}$

18. $P(3 \text{ or less, heads})$

> $\dfrac{1}{4}$

8-6
Experimental Probability

The table at the right shows the results of a survey.

19. How many people bought balloons? **75**

20. How many people were surveyed? **165**

21. What is the experimental probability that a person surveyed preferred balloons?

$\dfrac{5}{11}$

Item	Number of People
balloons	75
cards	15
decorations	25
cake	50

22. A bag contains 15 red marbles, 25 purple marbles, and 10 yellow marbles. Describe an experiment that you could conduct with the marbles to find an experimental probability.

Sample answer: Randomly pick marbles from the bag and record the results. Use these results to compute probabilities.

8-7
Using Sampling to Predict

23. What is the first step in conducting a survey?

Sample answer: Decide what type of sample of the population to use.

24. What you conduct a survey by asking ten students selected at random from each grade at your school what their favorite class is, what type of random sample have you taken?

unbiased, stratified sample

25. A grocery store owner asks the shoppers in his store where they prefer to shop for groceries. What type of sample has he conducted?

biased, convenience sample

ARE YOU READY FOR THE CHAPTER TEST?

Visit **msmath3.net** to access your textbook, more examples, self-check quizzes, and practice tests to help you study the concepts in Chapter 8.

Check the one that applies. Suggestions to help you study are given with each item.

☐ **I completed the review of all or most lessons without using my notes or asking for help.**

- You are probably ready for the Chapter Test.

- You may want to take the Chapter 8 Practice Test on page 413 of your textbook as a final check.

☐ **I used my Foldable or Study Notebook to complete the review of all or most lessons.**

- You should complete the Chapter 8 Study Guide and Review on pages 410–412 of your textbook.

- If you are unsure of any concepts or skills, refer back to the specific lesson(s).

- You may also want to take the Chapter 8 Practice Test on page 413.

☐ **I asked for help from someone else to complete the review of all or most lessons.**

- You should review the examples and concepts in your Study Notebook and Chapter 8 Foldable.

- Then complete the Chapter 8 Study Guide and Review on pages 410–412 of your textbook.

- If you are unsure of any concepts or skills, refer back to the specific lesson(s).

- You may also want to take the Chapter 8 Practice Test on page 413.

Student Signature

Parent/Guardian Signature

Teacher Signature

CHAPTER
9

Statistics and Matrices

 Use the instructions below to make a Foldable to help you organize your notes as you study the chapter. You will see Foldable reminders in the margin of this Interactive Study Notebook to help you in taking notes.

Begin with four pieces of $8\frac{1}{2}$" by 11" paper.

STEP 1 **Stack Pages**
Place 4 sheets of paper $\frac{3}{4}$ inch apart.

STEP 2 **Roll Up Bottom Edges**
All tabs should be the same size.

STEP 3 **Crease and Staple**
Staple along the fold.

STEP 4 **Label**
Label the tabs with topics from the chapter.

9-1 Histograms
9-2 Circle Graphs
9-3 Appropriate Display
9-4 Central Tendency
9-5 Measures of Variation
9-6 Box-and-Whisker
9-7 Misleading Statistics
9-8 Matrices

 NOTE-TAKING TIP: As you take notes on a topic, it helps to write how the subject relates to your life. For example, as you learn about different kinds of statistical measures and graphs, you will understand how to evaluate statistical information presented in such places as advertisements and persuasive articles in magazines.

BUILD YOUR VOCABULARY

This is an alphabetical list of new vocabulary terms you will learn in Chapter 9. As you complete the study notes for the chapter, you will see Build Your Vocabulary reminders to complete each term's definition or description on these pages. Remember to add the textbook page number in the second column for reference when you study.

Vocabulary Term	Found on Page	Definition	Description or Example
box-and-whisker plot			
circle graph			
column			
dimensions			
element			
histogram			
interquartile range			
lower quartile			
matrix [MAE-triks]			

Vocabulary Term	Found on Page	Definition	Description or Example
mean			
measures of central tendency			
measures of variation			
median			
mode			
outlier			
quartiles			
range			
row			
upper quartile			

Histograms

WHAT YOU'LL LEARN

• Construct and interpret histograms.

BUILD YOUR VOCABULARY (page 222)

A **histogram** is a type of | bar | graph used to display

numerical data that have been organized into

| equal | intervals.

ORGANIZE IT

Under the tab for Lesson 9–1, explain the difference between a bar graph and a histogram. Describe a type of statistics that could be displayed with a histogram.

EXAMPLE Draw a Histogram

1 FOOD The frequency table below shows the amount of caffeine in certain types of tea. Draw a histogram to represent the data.

Caffeine Content of Certain Types of Tea		
Caffeine (mg)	Tally	Frequency
1–20	卌 ‖	7
21–40	卌 ‖‖	8
41–60	‖	2
61–80		0
81–100	‖	2

Step 1 Draw and label a horizontal and vertical axis. Include a title.

Step 2 Show the | intervals | from the frequency table

on the | horizontal | axis.

Step 3 For each caffeine interval, draw a bar whose height is given by the frequencies.

Your Turn The frequency table below shows the amount of caffeine in certain drinks. Draw a histogram to represent the data.

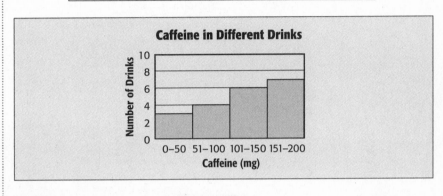

Caffeine Content of Certain Types of Drink		
Caffeine (mg)	Tally	Frequency
0–50	III	3
51–100	IIII	4
101–150	HHT I	6
151–200	HHT II	7

Caffeine in Different Drinks

[Histogram: Number of Drinks vs. Caffeine (mg)]

EXAMPLE Interpret Data

❷ WEATHER How many months had 6 or more days of rain?

Days of Rain Each Month

Three months had 6 to 7 days of rain, and one month had 8 to 9 days of rain.

Therefore, **3** + **1** or **4** months had 6 or more days of rain.

Your Turn How many months had 6 or more days of snow?

4 months

Days of Snow Each Month

EXAMPLE Compare Two Sets of Data

3 GRADES Determine which test had the greater number of students scoring 86 or higher.

On test 1, 6 + 14 + ⬚4⬚ or 24 students scored 86 or higher.

On test 2, ⬚16⬚ + 6 + 4 or 26 students scored 86 or higher.

A greater number of students scored 86 or higher on test 2.

Your Turn Determine which test had the greater number of students scoring 70 or higher.

Test 1

Circle Graphs

WHAT YOU'LL LEARN

- Construct and interpret circle graphs.

ORGANIZE IT

Under the tab for Lesson 9–2, find an example of a circle graph from a newspaper or magazine. Explain what the graph shows.

9-1 Histograms
9-2 Circle Graphs
9-3 Appropriate Display
9-4 Central Tendency
9-5 Measures of Variation
9-6 Box-and-Whisker
9-7 Misleading Statistics
9-8 Matrices

BUILD YOUR VOCABULARY (page 222)

A **circle graph** is used to compare parts of a ⟨ **whole** ⟩.

The entire ⟨ **circle** ⟩ represents that whole.

EXAMPLE Draw a Circle Graph

1 TORNADOES The table shows when tornadoes occurred in the United States from 1999 to 2001. Make a circle graph using this information.

Tornadoes in the United States, 1999–2001	
January–March	15%
April–June	53%
July–September	21%
October–December	11%

Source: spc.noaa.gov/

Step 1 There are ⟨ **360°** ⟩ in a circle. So, multiply each percent by 360 to find the number of degrees for each ⟨ **section** ⟩ of the graph.

Jan–Mar:

15% of 360 = ⟨ **0.15** ⟩ · 360 or ⟨ **54** ⟩

Apr–Jun:

53% of 360 = ⟨ **0.53** ⟩ · 360 or about ⟨ **191** ⟩

Jul–Sept:

21% of 360 = ⟨ **0.21** ⟩ · 360 or about ⟨ **76** ⟩

Oct–Dec:

11% of 360 = ⟨ **0.11** ⟩ · 360 or about ⟨ **40** ⟩

Step 2 Use a compass to draw a circle and a radius. Then use a protractor to draw a $\boxed{54°}$ angle. This section represents January–March. From the new radius, draw the next angle. Repeat for each of the remaining angles. Label each $\boxed{\textbf{section}}$. Then give the graph a $\boxed{\textbf{title}}$.

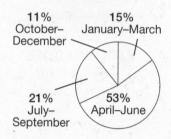

Tornadoes in the United States, 1999–2001

11% October–December
15% January–March
53% April–June
21% July–September

Your Turn The table shows when hurricanes or tropical storms occurred in the Atlantic Ocean during the hurricane season of 2002. Make a circle graph using this information.

Hurricanes in the United States, 2002	
Month	**Percent**
July	7%
August	21%
September	64%
October	8%

Source: nhc.noaa.gov/

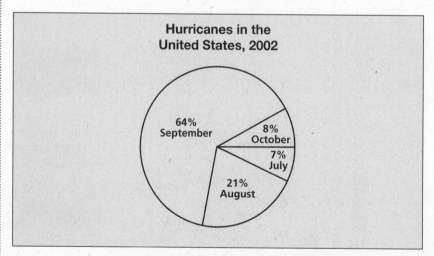

Hurricanes in the United States, 2002

64% September
8% October
7% July
21% August

EXAMPLES Use Circle Graphs to Interpret Data

2 BASKETBALL Make a circle graph using the information in the histogram below.

Average Points Per Basketball Game for Top 25 Scorers

Step 1 Find the total number of players.

$$6 + \boxed{12} + 1 + \boxed{4} + 2 = \boxed{25}$$

Step 2 Find the ratio that compares the number in each point range to the total number of players. Round to the nearest hundredth.

11.1 to 13 : $6 \div 25 = \boxed{0.24}$

13.1 to 15 : $12 \div 25 = \boxed{0.48}$

15.1 to 17 : $1 \div 25 = \boxed{0.04}$

17.1 to 19 : $4 \div 25 = \boxed{0.16}$

19.1 to 21 : $2 \div 25 = \boxed{0.08}$

Step 3 Use these ratios to find the number of degrees of each section. Round to the nearest degree if necessary.

11.1 to 13 : $\boxed{0.24} \cdot 360 = \boxed{86.4}$ or about $\boxed{86}$

13.1 to 15 : $\boxed{0.48} \cdot 360 = \boxed{172.8}$ or about 173

15.1 to 17 : $\boxed{0.04} \cdot 360 = \boxed{14.4}$ or about $\boxed{14}$

17.1 to 19 : $\boxed{0.16} \cdot 360 = \boxed{57.6}$ or about $\boxed{58}$

19.1 to 21 : $\boxed{0.08} \cdot 360 = \boxed{28.8}$ or about 29

© Glencoe/McGraw-Hill

Mathematics: Applications and Concepts, Course 3 **229**

Step 4 Use a compass and protractor to draw a circle and the appropriate sections. Label each section and give the graph a title. Write the ratios as percents.

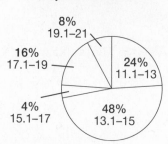

Average Points Per Basketball Game for Top 25 Scorers

❸ **Use the circle graph from Example 2 to describe the makeup of the average game scores of the 25 top-scoring basketball players.**

Almost $\frac{3}{4}$ of the players had average game scores between 11.1 and 15 points. Fewer than $\frac{1}{4}$ had average game scores greater than | 17 | points.

Your Turn

a. Make a circle graph using the information in the histogram at right.

Average Points Per Football Game for Top 10 Scorers

Average Points Per Football Game for Top 10 Scorers

b. Use the graph to describe the makeup of the average game scores of the 10 top-scoring football players.

Sample answer: More than one half of the players had game scores between 0 and 15. Ten percent had scores greater than 24.

HOMEWORK ASSIGNMENT

Page(s): _____

Exercises: _____

Choosing an Appropriate Display

WHAT YOU'LL LEARN

- Choose an appropriate display for a set of data.

FOLDABLES

ORGANIZE IT

Under the tab for Lesson 9–3, make a table of data from your science or social studies textbook. Draw a circle graph and bar graph displaying the data. Discuss which graph is most appropriate.

9-1 Histograms
9-2 Circle Graphs
9-3 Appropriate Display
9-4 Central Tendency
9-5 Measures of Variation
9-6 Box-and-Whisker
9-7 Misleading Statistics
9-8 Matrices

EXAMPLE Choose an Appropriate Display

Choose an appropriate type of display for each situation. Then make a display.

1 FARMS The table shows farm acres in Maine. Choose an appropriate display for this situation. Then make a display.

Farms in Maine by Size	
1–99 acres	46.8%
100–499 acres	43.8%
500–999 acres	6.9%
1,000 or more acres	2.5%

Source: ers.usda.gov

This data deals with percents that have a sum of **100%**.

A **circle graph** would be a good way to show percents.

Farms in Maine by Size

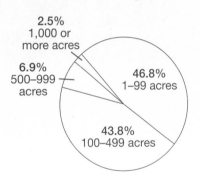

2.5%
1,000 or more acres

6.9%
500–999 acres

46.8%
1–99 acres

43.8%
100–499 acres

2 SCHOOL The results of a survey of a group of students asked to give their favorite school subject are shown in the table. Choose an appropriate type of display for this situation. Then make a display.

Favorite School Subject	
math	ⲐⲐ ⲐⲐ ⲐⲐ II
history	ⲐⲐ III
science	ⲐⲐ ⲐⲐ
English	ⲐⲐ II
other	ⲐⲐ I

In this case, there are specific categories. If you want to show the specific number, use a

bar graph or a **pictograph**.

Favorite School Subject

Mathematics: Applications and Concepts, Course 3   **231**

Your Turn

a. The table shows the favorite type of television program of students at Walnut Junior High. Choose an appropriate type of display for this situation. Then make a display.

Favorite Type of Television Program	
sitcom	54%
reality	22%
news	10%
game show	8%
cartoon	6%

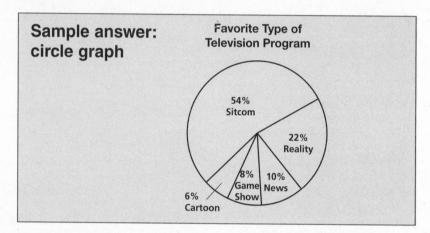

Sample answer: circle graph

Favorite Type of Television Program

54% Sitcom
22% Reality
10% News
8% Game Show
6% Cartoon

b. The results of a survey of a group of students asked to give their favorite hobby are shown below. Choose an appropriate type of display for this situation. Then make a display.

Hobby	Number of Students
reading	10
sports	5
listening to music	10
photography	7
other	18

Sample answer: bar graph

Favorite Hobbies

HOMEWORK ASSIGNMENT

Page(s): _____

Exercises: _____

WHAT YOU'LL LEARN

- Find the mean, median, and mode of a set of data.

WRITE IT

The words *central* and *middle* have similar definitions. If mean, median, and mode are measures of central tendency, what do they measure?

_____

_____

_____

_____

BUILD YOUR VOCABULARY (page 223)

Measures of central tendency are numbers that

| describe | a set of data.

The **mean** of a set of data is the | sum | of the data

| divided by | the number of items in the data set.

The **median** of a set of data is the | middle | number of the data ordered from least to greatest, or the

mean of the | middle two | numbers.

The **mode** of a set of data is the number or numbers that

occur | most | often.

EXAMPLE Find Measures of Central Tendency

1 Find the mean, median, and mode of the set of data.
4, 16, 32, 19, 27, 32

Mean $\dfrac{4 + 16 + 32 + 19 + 27 + 32}{\boxed{6}} = \boxed{\dfrac{130}{6}}$

$\approx \boxed{21.7}$

Median Arrange the numbers in order from | least |

to | greatest |.

4   16   19   27   32   32

$\dfrac{\boxed{19} + \boxed{27}}{\boxed{2}} = \boxed{23}$

Mode The data has a mode of $\boxed{32}$.

Your Turn Find the mean, median, and mode of the set of data. 3, 5, 3, 7, 6, 4

mean: 4.7; median: 4.5; mode: 3

EXAMPLES Using Appropriate Measures

OLYMPICS Use the table to answer each question.

Gold Medals Won by the United States at the Winter Olympics, 1924–2002			
Event	Gold Medals	Event	Gold Medals
Alpine skiing	10	Luge	2
Bobsleigh	6	Short track speed skating	3
Cross country	0	Skeleton	3
Figure skating	13	Ski jumping	0
Freestyle skiing	4	Snowboarding	2
Ice hockey	3	Speed skating	26

FOLDABLES

ORGANIZE IT

Under the tab for Lesson 9–4, record how to find the mean, median, and mode of a set of data. Explain *measures of central tendency, mean, median,* and *mode* in your own words and with examples.

9-1 Histograms
9-2 Circle Graphs
9-3 Appropriate Display
9-4 Central Tendency
9-5 Measures of Variation
9-6 Box-and-Whisker
9-7 Misleading Statistics
9-8 Matrices

2 What is the mean, median, and mode of the data?

Mean $\dfrac{10 + 6 + 0 + 13 + 4 + 3 + 2 + 3 + 3 + 0 + 2 + 26}{\boxed{12}} = \dfrac{\boxed{72}}{\boxed{12}}$

$= \boxed{6}$

The mean is $\boxed{6}$ medals.

Median Arrange the numbers from least to greatest.

0, 0, 2, 2, 3, 3, 3, 4, 6, 10, 13, 26

The median is the middle number, or $\boxed{3}$ medals.

Mode There is one mode, $\boxed{3}$.

3 Which measure of central tendency is most representative of the data?

The median and the mode; the mean is affected by the extreme value of $\boxed{26}$. The mode is the same as the median. So, both the median and the mode are good choices.

Your Turn Use the table to answer each question.

Country	Gold Medals (1896–2002 Summer)
United States	872
Great Britain	180
France	188
Italy	179
Sweden	136
Hungary	150
Australia	102
Finland	101
Japan	97
Romania	74
Brazil	12
Ethiopia	12

Source: infoplease.com

a. What is the mean, median, and mode of the data?

> **mean: 175.25;**
> **median: 119;**
> **mode: 12**

b. Which measure of central tendency is the most
representative of the data?

> **The median; the mean is affected by the extreme**
> **value of 872 and the mode is much lower than**
> **the rest of the data.**

HOMEWORK
ASSIGNMENT

Page(s):

Exercises:

Measures of Variation

WHAT YOU'LL LEARN

- Find the range and quartiles of a set of data.

KEY CONCEPTS

Range The range of a set of data is the difference between the greatest and the least numbers in the set.

Interquartile Range The interquartile range is the range of the middle half of the data. It is the difference between the upper quartile and the lower quartile.

BUILD YOUR VOCABULARY (pages 222–223)

Measures of variation are used to describe the

distribution of a set of data.

The **range** indicates how **spread out** the data are.

Quartiles are the values that divide the data into

four equal parts.

The **median** of the lower half of a set of data is the

lower quartile.

The median of the **upper half** of the set of data is the **upper quartile**.

Data that are more than **1.5** times the value of the interquartile range beyond the quartiles are called **outliers**.

EXAMPLES Find Measures of Variation

BASKETBALL Use the table at the right.

1 Find the range of the scores.

The greatest number of scores is **109**.

The least number of scores is **91.3**.

The range is

109 – **91.3** or

17.7 points.

Points Scored by Top Ten Teams During the NBA Playoffs, 2002	
Team	**Points Scored**
Dallas	109
Minnesota	102
Sacramento	101.1
L.A. Lakers	97.8
Charlotte	96.1
New Jersey	95.4
Orlando	93.8
Indiana	91.6
Boston	91.3
Portland	91.3

Source: nba.com

2 **Find the median and the upper and lower quartiles of the scores.**

Arrange the numbers in order from least to greatest.

lower quartile   median   upper quartile

91.3 91.3 **91.6** 93.8 95.4 96.1 97.8 **101.1** 102 109

$$\frac{95.4 + 96.1}{2} = \boxed{95.75}$$

The median is **95.75** , the lower quartile is **91.6** , and

the upper quartile is **101.1** .

REMEMBER IT

A small interquartile range means that the data in the middle of the set are close in value. A large interquartile range means that the data in the middle are spread out.

3 **Find the interquartile range of the scores.**

Interquartile Range: **101.1** – **91.6** or **9.5**

Your Turn Use the table at the right.

a. Find the range of the batting averages.

0.269

b. Find the median and the upper and lower quartiles of the batting averages.

median: 0.290; upper quartile: 0.407; lower quartile: 0.250

Giants Batting Average Against Anaheim in the World Series 2002	
Player	Batting Average
Rueter	0.500
Bonds	0.471
Snow	0.407
Bell	0.304
Lofton	0.290
Kent	0.276
Aurilia	0.250
Sanders	0.238
Santiago	0.231

Source: infoplease.com

c. Find the interquartile range of the batting averages.

0.157

EXAMPLE Find Outliers

FOLDABLES

ORGANIZE IT

Under the tab for Lesson 9–5, write what you learn about finding the range and quartiles of a set of data.

9-1 Histograms
9-2 Circle Graphs
9-3 Appropriate Display
9-4 Central Tendency
9-5 Measures of Variation
9-6 Box-and-Whisker
9-7 Misleading Statistics
9-8 Matrices

④ CONCESSION SALES
Find any outliers for the data in the table at the right.

First arrange the numbers in order from least to greatest. Then find the median, upper quartile, and lower quartile.

Items Sold at Football Game Concession Stand	
Item	**Number Sold**
Colas	196
Diet colas	32
Water	46
Coffee	18
Candy bars	39
Hotdogs	23
Hamburgers	16
Chips	41
Popcorn	24

16   18   23   24   32   39   41   46   196

$$\frac{18 + 23}{2} = \boxed{20.5} \qquad 32 \qquad \frac{41 + 46}{2} = \boxed{43.5}$$

Interquartile Range = $\boxed{43.5}$ – $\boxed{20.5}$ or 23

Multiply the interquartile range, 23, by 1.5.

$\boxed{23} \times \boxed{1.5} = 34.5$

Find the limits for the outliers.

Subtract 34.5 from the lower quartile. $\boxed{20.5}$ – 34.5 = $\boxed{-14}$

Add 34.5 to the upper quartile. $\boxed{43.5}$ + 34.5 = $\boxed{78}$

The limits for the outliers are $\boxed{-14}$ and $\boxed{78}$.

The only outlier is $\boxed{196}$.

HOMEWORK ASSIGNMENT

Page(s): _____
Exercises: _____

Your Turn Find any outliers for the data in the table at right.

93

Items Sold at School Bookstore	
Item	**Number Sold**
Pens	35
Pencils	15
Erasers	20
Candy bars	93
Folders	17
School Pennants	18
Calculators	2

Box-and-Whisker Plots

WHAT YOU'LL LEARN

- Display and interpret data in a box-and-whisker plot.

FOLDABLES

ORGANIZE IT

Under the tab for Lesson 9–6, collect data from the Internet, such as number of homeruns hit by the players of a baseball team. Draw a box-and-whisker plot to display the data.

9-1 Histograms
9-2 Circle Graphs
9-3 Appropriate Display
9-4 Central Tendency
9-5 Measures of Variation
9-6 Box-and-Whisker
9-7 Misleading Statistics
9-8 Matrices

BUILD YOUR VOCABULARY (page 222)

A **box-and-whisker plot** uses a [number line] to show the [distribution] of a set of data.

EXAMPLE Draw a Box-and-Whisker Plot

1 POPULATION Use the data in the table at the right to draw a box-and-whisker plot.

World's Most Populous Cities	
City	Population (millions)
Tokyo	34.8
New York	20.2
Seoul	19.9
Mexico City	19.8
Sao Paulo	17.9
Bombay	17.9
Osaka	17.9
Los Angeles	16.2
Cairo	14.4
Manila	13.5

Source: *Time Almanac*

Step 1 Draw a [number line] that includes the least and greatest number in the data.

Step 2 Mark the extremes, the [median], and the upper and lower [quartile] above the number line. Since the data have an outlier, mark the greatest value that is not an [outlier].

Step 3 Draw the box and whiskers.

Your Turn

Use the data in the table at the right to draw a box-and-whisker plot.

Most Populous U.S. Cities	
City	Population (in millions)
New York	8.0
Los Angeles	3.7
Chicago	2.9
Houston	2.0
Philadelphia	1.5
Phoenix	1.3
San Diego	1.2
Dallas	1.2

Source: infoplease.com

EXAMPLE Interpret Data

2 **WATERFALLS** What does the length of the box-and-whisker plot below tell you about the data?

Highest Waterfalls in the
World (thousands of feet)

Source: *Time Almanac*

Data in the **second** quartile are more spread out than the

data in the **third** quartile. You can see that data in the

fourth quartile are the most spread out because the

whisker is **longer** than other parts of the plot.

Your Turn What does the length of the box-and-whisker plot below tell you about the data?

Number of Hours Spent Exercising Each Week

Data in the second quartile are less spread out than the data in the third quartile. You can see that data in the third quartile are the most spread out because the box is longer than other parts of the plot.

HOMEWORK ASSIGNMENT

Page(s): _____

Exercises: _____

_____

_____

WHAT YOU'LL LEARN

- Recognize when graphs and statistics are misleading.

ORGANIZE IT

Under the tab for Lesson 9–7 record what you learn about recognizing misleading statistics or graphs. Try to collect an example of misleading statistics or graphs in print. Glue or tape them into your Foldable and explain how and why they are misleading.

9-1 Histograms
9-2 Circle Graphs
9-3 Appropriate Display
9-4 Central Tendency
9-5 Measures of Variation
9-6 Box-and-Whisker
9-7 Misleading Statistics
9-8 Matrices

EXAMPLE Identify a Misleading Graph

1 TELEVISIONS Which graph below could be used to indicate a greater difference in number of televisions? Explain.

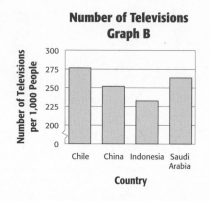

Both graphs show the order from greatest to least number of televisions per 1,000 people in Chile, Saudi Arabia, China, and Indonesia. However, the intervals in graph B represent

| 200 to 300 | instead of | 0 to 600 | like graph A.

Graph B shows a greater difference in televisions.

Your Turn Which graph below could be used to show a greater difference in favorite classes?

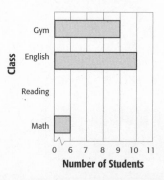

> **Graph B because the interval does not start at 0.**

EXAMPLES Identify Different Uses of Statistics

GYMNASTICS The scores for girls on a team competing on vault at a meet are 8.3, 8.5, 8.5, 8.8, 9.0, and 9.2.

2 Find the mean, median, and mode of the vault scores.

Mean $\dfrac{\text{sum of values}}{\text{number of values}} = \dfrac{52.3}{6}$ or about   **8.72**

Median $\dfrac{8.5 + 8.8}{2} = \dfrac{17.3}{2}$ or   **8.65**

Mode   **8.5**

3 Which average would the team use to make its results look the best? Explain.

A gymnastics team would most likely want to show the highest

average in scores. The   **mean**   shows the highest

event score,   **8.72** .

Your Turn   The scores for girls on a team competing in the short program are 5.2, 5.5, 5.5, 5.9, 5.8, and 6.0.

a. Find the mean, median, and mode of the scores.

> **mean: 5.65; median: 5.65; mode: 5.5**

b. Which average would the team use to make its results look the best? Explain.

> **Mean or median; both are 5.65 and show the highest average score.**

HOMEWORK ASSIGNMENT

Page(s): _____

Exercises: _____

WHAT YOU'LL LEARN

- Use matrices to organize data.

© Glencoe/McGraw-Hill

BUILD YOUR VOCABULARY (pages 222–223)

A **rectangular** arrangement of numerical data is called a **matrix**.

$$\begin{bmatrix} 7 & -9 & 2 \\ -4 & 0 & 1 \\ 5 & 6 & -8 \end{bmatrix}$$

In a matrix, the numbers side by side **horizontally** form a **row**.

In a matrix, the numbers **vertically** under one another form a **column**.

Each **number** in a matrix is called an **element**.

A matrix is described by its **dimensions**, or the number of **rows** and **columns**.

FOLDABLES

ORGANIZE IT

Under the tab for Lesson 9–8, list 2 or 3 matrices. Label the row and columns and give the dimensions.

9-1 Histograms
9-2 Circle Graphs
9-3 Appropriate Display
9-4 Central Tendency
9-5 Measures of Variation
9-6 Box-and-Whisker
9-7 Misleading Statistics
9-8 Matrices

EXAMPLE Identify Dimensions and Elements

1 State the dimensions of $\begin{bmatrix} -3 & 2 & 8 \\ ① & -6 & 5 \\ 6 & -1 & 12 \end{bmatrix}$. Then identify

the position of the circled element.

The matrix has **3** rows and **3** columns. The dimensions

of the matrix are **3 by 3**.

The circled element is in the **second** row and the **first** column.

EXAMPLES Add and Subtract Matrices

Add or subtract. If there is no sum or difference, write *impossible*.

2 $\begin{bmatrix} -5 & -2 & -1 \\ 8 & 1 & -3 \end{bmatrix} + \begin{bmatrix} 2 & 3 & -2 \\ -2 & 7 & 9 \end{bmatrix}$

$\begin{bmatrix} -5 & -2 & -1 \\ 8 & 1 & -3 \end{bmatrix} + \begin{bmatrix} 2 & 3 & -2 \\ -2 & 7 & 9 \end{bmatrix} = \begin{bmatrix} -5+2 & -2+3 & -1+(-2) \\ 8+(-2) & \boxed{1+7} & \boxed{-3+9} \end{bmatrix}$

$= \begin{bmatrix} -3 & 1 & -3 \\ 6 & \boxed{8} & \boxed{6} \end{bmatrix}$

3 $\begin{bmatrix} -3 & -3 \\ 8 & 2 \end{bmatrix} - [96]$

The first matrix has $\boxed{2}$ rows and $\boxed{2}$ columns. The second matrix has $\boxed{1}$ row and $\boxed{1}$ column. Since the matrices do not have the same $\boxed{\text{dimensions}}$, it is $\boxed{\text{impossible}}$ to subtract them.

4 $\begin{bmatrix} 3 & 2 & -8 & 6 \\ 5 & 12 & 4 & -2 \\ 7 & -3 & 8 & 2 \\ 6 & 1 & 1 & -6 \end{bmatrix} - \begin{bmatrix} 2 & 1 & 7 & 2 \\ -2 & -3 & 2 & 5 \\ 4 & 1 & 6 & -2 \\ 2 & 9 & 12 & -4 \end{bmatrix}$

$= \begin{bmatrix} 3-2 & 2-1 & \boxed{-8-7} & 6-2 \\ 5-(-2) & \boxed{12-(-3)} & 4-2 & \boxed{-2-5} \\ 7-4 & -3-1 & \boxed{8-6} & 2-(-2) \\ \boxed{6-2} & 1-9 & 1-12 & \boxed{-6-(-4)} \end{bmatrix}$

$= \begin{bmatrix} \boxed{1} & 1 & \boxed{-15} & 4 \\ 7 & 15 & \boxed{2} & \boxed{-7} \\ 3 & \boxed{-4} & 2 & 4 \\ 4 & -8 & -11 & \boxed{-2} \end{bmatrix}$

Your Turn

a. State the dimensions of $\begin{bmatrix} -2 & 5 & \boxed{0} \\ 3 & -6 & -4 \end{bmatrix}$. Then identify the position of the circled element.

> **2 by 3; first row, third column**

Add or subtract. If there is no sum or difference, write *impossible*.

b. $\begin{bmatrix} -2 & -1 & -4 \\ 5 & 1 & 2 \end{bmatrix} + \begin{bmatrix} 3 & 5 & 2 \\ 3 & -2 & 0 \end{bmatrix}$

> $\begin{bmatrix} 1 & 4 & -2 \\ 8 & -1 & 2 \end{bmatrix}$

c. $\begin{bmatrix} 2 & 2 \\ 5 & 1 \end{bmatrix} - \begin{bmatrix} -4 & 6 & -7 \\ 3 & 0 & 11 \end{bmatrix}$

> **impossible**

d. $\begin{bmatrix} 2 & -1 & -8 & 3 \\ 1 & -6 & 4 & -2 \\ 4 & -3 & 7 & 2 \\ 6 & 2 & 0 & -6 \end{bmatrix} - \begin{bmatrix} 2 & 1 & 3 & 2 \\ -2 & -3 & 2 & 6 \\ 8 & 2 & 7 & -2 \\ 6 & 4 & 11 & 0 \end{bmatrix}$

> $\begin{bmatrix} 0 & -2 & -11 & 1 \\ 3 & -3 & 2 & -8 \\ -4 & -5 & 0 & 4 \\ 0 & -2 & -11 & -6 \end{bmatrix}$

HOMEWORK ASSIGNMENT

Page(s): _____

Exercises: _____

_____

_____

© Glencoe/McGraw-Hill

BRINGING IT ALL TOGETHER

STUDY GUIDE

FOLDABLES™	**VOCABULARY PUZZLEMAKER**	**BUILD YOUR VOCABULARY**
Use your **Chapter 9 Foldable** to help you study for your chapter test.	To make a crossword puzzle, word search, or jumble puzzle of the vocabulary words in Chapter 9, go to: www.glencoe.com/sec/math/t_resources/free/index.php	You can use your completed **Vocabulary Builder** *(pages 222–223)* to help you solve the puzzle.

9-1

Histograms

1. Explain the difference between a bar graph and a histogram.

> **A histogram is a type of bar graph with the data organized into equal intervals and with no spaces between bars.**

Use the histogram at the right.

2. How many months have less than two days of rain? **4**

3. How many months had between two and seven days of rain? **7**

Days of Rain Each Month

9-2

Circle Graphs

Use the circle graph at the right.

4. What percent of her time does Luisa spend studying? **13%**

5. How many degrees are in the section that represents sports?

20°

Luisa's Day
8% Meals
8% Sports
13% Study
13% Other
25% School
33% Sleep

9-3

Choosing an Appropriate Display

Choose the letter that best matches the type of display to its use.

6. Line Graph **d** **a.** shows the frequency of data that has been organized into equal intervals

7. Bar Graph **c** **b.** shows the number of items in specific categories in the data using bars

8. Histogram **a** **c.** shows change over a period of time

9. Line Plot **c** **d.** shows how many times each number occurs in the data

9-4

Measures of Central Tendency

10. Name the three most common measures of central tendency.

mean, median, and mode

11. Which measure of central tendency best represents the data? Why? 9, 9, 20, 22, 25, 27

The mode of 9 is much lower than the other values. The mean is 18.66, which is below most of the values. So, the median of 21 best represents the data.

9-5

Measures of Variation

Complete.

12. Measures of variation describe the **distribution** of data.

13. The **range** of a set of data is the difference between the greatest and the least numbers in the set.

14. The **interquartile** range is the difference between the upper and lower quartiles.

9-6

Box-and-Whisker Plots

15. Draw a box-and-whisker plot for the data. 1, 1, 1, 2, 3, 3, 4, 5, 5

1 2 3 4 5

9-7

Misleading Graphs and Statistics

16. When writing an employment ad for an automotive dealership, would it be best to use the mean, median, or mode of the number of cars sold to encourage a commissioned salesperson to apply for the job?

Wagner Automotive Sales			
Month	Cars Sold	Month	Cars Sold
Jan.	16	July	44
Feb.	5	Aug.	40
March	34	Sept.	38
April	49	Oct.	45
May	47	Nov.	48
June	79	Dec.	38

median

9-8

Matrices

17. Describe the matrix $\begin{bmatrix} 26 & 45 & 36 & 14 \\ 5 & 4 & 9 & 3 \end{bmatrix}$ in terms of its

dimensions. **2 by 4**

18. Before you can add or subtract two matrices, what must be the same? Explain.

The dimensions must be the same. Sample answer: so that the elements can be paired.

19. What is each number of a matrix called?

element

20. Find $\begin{bmatrix} 2 & -5 & 3 \\ 4 & 1 & -9 \end{bmatrix} + \begin{bmatrix} 0 & 7 & -8 \\ 1 & -6 & -9 \end{bmatrix}$.

$\begin{bmatrix} 2 & 2 & -5 \\ 5 & -5 & -18 \end{bmatrix}$

ARE YOU READY FOR THE CHAPTER TEST?

Math Online

Visit **msmath3.net** to access your textbook, more examples, self-check quizzes, and practice tests to help you study the concepts in Chapter 9.

Check the one that applies. Suggestions to help you study are given with each item.

☐ **I completed the review of all or most lessons without using my notes or asking for help.**

- You are probably ready for the Chapter Test.
- You may want to take the Chapter 9 Practice Test on page 461 of your textbook as a final check.

☐ **I used my Foldable or Study Notebook to complete the review of all or most lessons.**

- You should complete the Chapter 9 Study Guide and Review on pages 458–460 of your textbook.
- If you are unsure of any concepts or skills, refer back to the specific lesson(s).
- You may also want to take the Chapter 9 Practice Test on page 461.

☐ **I asked for help from someone else to complete the review of all or most lessons.**

- You should review the examples and concepts in your Study Notebook and Chapter 9 Foldable.
- Then complete the Chapter 9 Study Guide and Review on pages 458-460 of your textbook.
- If you are unsure of any concepts or skills, refer back to the specific lesson(s).
- You may also want to take the Chapter 9 Practice Test on page 461.

Student Signature

Parent/Guardian Signature

Teacher Signature

Algebra: More Equations and Inequalities

Use the instructions below to make a Foldable to help you organize your notes as you study the chapter. You will see Foldable reminders in the margin of this Interactive Study Notebook to help you in taking notes.

Begin with a plain sheet of 11" × 17" paper.

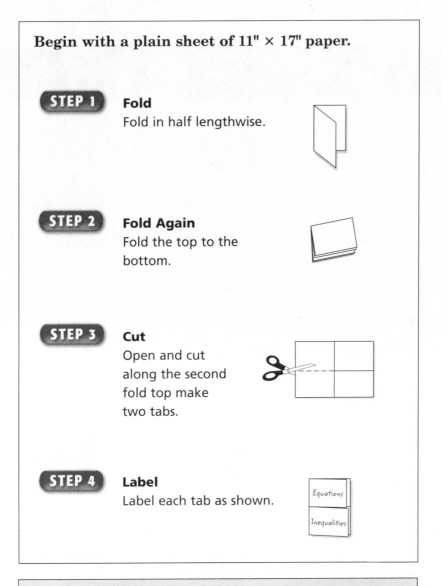

STEP 1   **Fold**
Fold in half lengthwise.

STEP 2   **Fold Again**
Fold the top to the bottom.

STEP 3   **Cut**
Open and cut along the second fold top make two tabs.

STEP 4   **Label**
Label each tab as shown.

Equations

Inequalities

NOTE-TAKING TIP: When you take notes, define new terms and write about the new concepts you are learning in your own words. Write your own examples that use the new terms and concepts.

This is an alphabetical list of new vocabulary terms you will learn in Chapter 10. As you complete the study notes for the chapter, you will see Build Your Vocabulary reminders to complete each term's definition or description on these pages. Remember to add the textbook page number in the second column for reference when you study.

Vocabulary Term	Found on Page	Definition	Description or Example
coefficient			
constant			
equivalent expressions			
like terms			
simplest form			
simplifying the expression			
term			
two-step equation			

Simplifying Algebraic Expressions

WHAT YOU'LL LEARN

• Use the Distributive Property to simplify algebraic expressions.

BUILD YOUR VOCABULARY (page 252)

Equivalent expressions are expressions that have the
| same value | regardless of the value of the variable.

EXAMPLE Write Equivalent Expressions

1 Use the Distributive Property to rewrite $3(x + 5)$.

$3(x + 5) = 3(x) + 3(5)$

$\qquad = 3x + \boxed{15}$ \qquad Simplify.

Your Turn Use the Distributive Property to rewrite each expression.

a. $2(x + 6)$

$\boxed{2x + 12}$

b. $(a + 6)3$

$\boxed{3a + 18}$

EXAMPLES Write Expressions with Subtraction

Use the Distributive Property to rewrite each expression. **(parallels Example 3 in text)**

2 $(q - 3)9$

$(q - 3)\,9 = [q + (-3)]\,9$ \qquad Rewrite $q - 3$ as $q + (-3)$

$\qquad = (\boxed{q})\,9 + (\boxed{-3})9$ \quad Distributive Property.

$\qquad = \boxed{9q} + (\boxed{-27})$ \qquad Simplify.

$\qquad = \boxed{9q} - \boxed{27}$ \qquad Definition of subtraction.

3 $-3(z - 7)$ \qquad **(parallels Example 4 in text)**

$-3(z - 7) = -3\,[z + (-7)]$ \qquad Rewrite $z - 7$ as $z + (-7)$.

$\qquad = -3(z) + (-3)(-7)$ \qquad Distributive Property

$\qquad = -3z + \boxed{21}$ \qquad Simplify.

REVIEW IT

What is the sign of the product when you multiply two integers with different signs? with the same sign?
(Lesson 1-6)

_____

_____

_____

_____

Your Turn Use the Distributive Property to rewrite each expression.

a. $(q - 2)\,8$

$8q - 16$

b. $-2(z - 4)$

$-2z + 8$

BUILD YOUR VOCABULARY (page 252)

When a plus sign separates an algebraic expression into parts, each part is called a **term**.

The numeric factor of a term that contains a **variable** is called the **coefficient** of the variable.

Like terms are terms that contain the **same** variable.

A term without a **variable** is called a **constant**.

EXAMPLE Identify Parts of an Expression (parallels Example 5 in text)

4 Identify the terms, like terms, coefficients, and constants in $3x - 5 + 2x - x$.

$3x - 5 + 2x - x$

$= 3x + (\boxed{-5}) + 2x + (\boxed{-x})$ Definition of Subtraction

$= 3x + (-5) + 2x + (-1x)$ Identity Property; $-x = -1x$

The terms are $3x$, $\boxed{-5}$, $2x$, and $-x$. The like terms are $3x$,

$2x$, and $\boxed{-x}$. The coefficients are 3, $\boxed{2}$, and -1. The

constant is $\boxed{-5}$.

Your Turn Identify the terms, like terms, coefficients, and constants in $6x - 2 + x - 4x$.

The terms are $6x$, -2, x, and $-4x$. The like terms are $6x$, x, and $-4x$. The coefficients are 6, 1, and -4. The constant is -2.

BUILD YOUR VOCABULARY (page 252)

An algebraic expression is in **simplest form** if it has no

$\boxed{\text{like terms}}$ and no $\boxed{\text{parentheses}}$.

When you use properties to $\boxed{\text{combine}}$ like terms you
are **simplifying the expression**.

EXAMPLES Simplify Algebraic Expressions

Simplify each expression. **(parallels Example 6 in text)**

5 $6n - n$

$6n$ and n are $\boxed{\text{like}}$ terms.

$6n - n = 6n - \boxed{1n}$ Identity Property; $n = \boxed{1n}$

$\quad\quad = (6-1)n$ Distributive Property

$\quad\quad = \boxed{5n}$ Simplify.

6 $8z + z - 5 - 9z + 2$ **(parallels Example 8 in text)**

$8z$, z, and $\boxed{-9z}$ are like terms. 5 and $\boxed{2}$ are also like terms.

$8z + z - 5 - 9z + 2$

$\quad = 8z + z + (\boxed{-5}) + (\boxed{-9x}) + 2$ Definition of subtraction.

$\quad = 8z + z + (-9z) + (-5) + 2$ Commutative Property

$\quad = [8 + 1 + (-9)]\boxed{z} + [(-5) + 2]$ Distributive Property

$\quad = 0z + \boxed{(-3)}$ Simplify.

$\quad = \boxed{-3}$

HOMEWORK ASSIGNMENT

Page(s):

Exercises:

Your Turn Simplify each expression.

a. $7n + n$

$\boxed{8n}$

b. $6s + 2 - 10s$

$\boxed{-4s + 2}$

c. $6z + z - 2 - 8z + 2$

$\boxed{-z}$

Solving Two-Step Equations

WHAT YOU'LL LEARN

- Solve two-step equations.

A **two-step equation** contains [**two operations**].

EXAMPLE Solve a Two-Step Equation

REMEMBER IT

Two-step equations can also be solved using models. Refer to page 474 of your textbook.

1 Solve $5x + 1 = 26$.

Use the Subtraction Property of Equality.

$5x + 1 = 26$ Write the equation.

[−1]   [−1]   Subtract [1] from each side.

$5x \quad = 25$

Use the Division Property of Equality.

$5x \quad = \quad 25$

$\dfrac{5x}{[\,5\,]} = \dfrac{25}{[\,5\,]}$ Divide each side by [5].

$x = [\,5\,]$ Simplify.

Your Turn   Solve $3x + 2 = 20$.

[6]

EXAMPLES Solve Two- Step Equations

2 Solve $2n - 8 = 34$.

$2n - 8 = 34$ Write the equation.

$2n - 8 + [\,8\,] = 34 + [\,8\,]$ Add [8] to each side.

$\dfrac{2n}{[\,2\,]} = \dfrac{42}{[\,2\,]}$ Simplify. Divide each side by [2].

$n = 21$ Simplify.

3 Solve $-4 = \frac{1}{3}z + 2$.

$$-4 = \frac{1}{3}z + 2$$ Write the equation.

$$-4 - \boxed{2} = \frac{1}{3}z + 2 - \boxed{2}$$ Subtract $\boxed{2}$ from each side.

$$-6 = \frac{1}{3}z$$ Simplify.

$$\boxed{3}(-6) = \boxed{3} \cdot \frac{1}{3}z$$ Multiply each side by $\boxed{3}$.

$$-18 = z$$ Simplify.

Your Turn Solve each equation.

a. $5n - 6 = 39$

9

b. $-5 = \frac{1}{2}z + 8$

-26

EXAMPLE Equations with Negative Coefficients

4 Solve $8 - 3x = 14$.

REMEMBER IT

When you are solving an equation, watch for the negative signs. In Example 4, the coefficient of the variable, x, is -3, not $+3$. So, divide each side by -3 to solve for x.

$$8 - 3x = 14$$ Write the equation.

$$8 + (\boxed{-3x}) = 14$$ Definition of subtraction.

$$8 - 8 + (\boxed{-3x}) = 14 - 8$$ Subtract 8 from each side.

$$-3x = 6$$ Simplify.

$$\frac{-3x}{\boxed{-3}} = \frac{6}{\boxed{-3}}$$ Divide each side by $\boxed{-3}$.

$$x = -2$$ Simplify.

Your Turn Solve $5 - 2x = 11$.

-3

EXAMPLE Combine Like Terms Before Solving

5 Solve $14 = -k + 3k - 2$.

$14 = -k + 3k - 2$ Write the equation.

$14 = -1k + 3k - 2$ **Identity** Property; $-k = 1k$

$14 = \boxed{\textbf{2k}} - 2$ Combine like terms;

                $-1k + 3k = (-1 + 3)k$ or $2k$.

$14 + \boxed{\textbf{2}} = 2k - 2 + \boxed{\textbf{2}}$ Add $\boxed{\textbf{2}}$ to each side.

$16 = 2k$ Simplify.

$\dfrac{16}{\boxed{\textbf{2}}} = \dfrac{2k}{\boxed{\textbf{2}}}$ Divide each side by $\boxed{\textbf{2}}$.

$8 = k$ Simplify.

Your Turn Solve $10 = -n + 4n - 5$.

5

Writing Two-Step Equations

© Glencoe/McGraw-Hill

WHAT YOU'LL LEARN

• Write two-step equations that represent real-life situations.

REVIEW IT

What are at least two words that will tell you that a sentence can be written as an equation? *(Lesson 1-7)*

_____

_____

_____

_____

_____

_____

EXAMPLES Translate Sentences Into Equations

Translate each sentence into an equation.

Sentence	Equation
1 Three more than a half a number is 15.	$\frac{1}{2}n +$ ⟨ **3** ⟩ $= 15$
2 Nineteen is two more than five times a number.	$19 =$ ⟨ **5n** ⟩ $+ 2$
3 Eight less that twice a number is -35.	⟨ **2n** ⟩ $- 8 = -35$

EXAMPLE Translate and Solve an Equation

4 Two more than $\frac{1}{3}$ of a number is 6. Find the number.

Words	Two more than $\frac{1}{3}$ of a number is 6.
▼	
Variable	Let $n =$ the number.
▼	
Equation	$\frac{1}{3}n + 2 =$ ⟨ **6** ⟩

$\frac{1}{3}n + 2 = 6$ Write the equation.

$\frac{1}{3}n + 2 -$ ⟨ **2** ⟩ $= 6 -$ ⟨ **2** ⟩   Subtract ⟨ **2** ⟩ from each side.

$\frac{1}{3}n =$ ⟨ **4** ⟩   Simplify.

$n =$ ⟨ **12** ⟩   Mentally multiply each side by ⟨ **3** ⟩.

The number is ⟨ **12** ⟩.

ORGANIZE IT

Record the main ideas, definitions of vocabulary words, and other notes as you learn how to write two-step equations. Write your notes under the "Equations" tab.

Equations

Inequalities

EXAMPLE Write and Solve a Two-Step Equation

5 TRANSPORTATION A taxi ride costs $3.50 plus $2 for each mile traveled. If Jan pays $11.50 for the ride, how many miles did she travel?

Her costs start at $3.50 and adds $2 until it reaches $11.50. Organize tha data for the first few miles into a table and look for a pattern.

Miles	Cost
0	$3.50 + 2(0) = 3.50$
1	$3.50 + 2(1) = 5.50$
2	$3.50 + 2(2) = 7.50$
3	$3.50 + 2(3) = 9.50$

Write an equation to represent the situation. Let m represent the number of miles.

flat rate	plus	m miles at $2 per mile	equals	$11.50
3.50	+	**$2m$**	=	11.50

$$\boxed{3.50} + \boxed{2m} = 11.50$$ Write the equation.

$$3.50 - \boxed{3.50} + 2m = 11.50 - \boxed{3.50}$$ Subtract $\boxed{3.50}$ from each side.

$$2m = 8$$ Simplify.

$$\frac{\boxed{2m}}{\boxed{2}} = \frac{\boxed{8}}{\boxed{2}}$$ Divide each side by $\boxed{2}$.

$$m = \boxed{4}$$ Simplify.

Jan traveled $\boxed{4}$ miles.

Your Turn Translate each sentence into an equation.

a. Five more than one third
a number is 7.

$$\frac{1}{3}n + 5 = 7$$

b. Fifteen is three more than
six times a number.

$$15 = 6n + 3$$

c. Six less that three times
a number is −22.

$$3n − 6 = −22$$

d. Three more than six times a number is 15. Find the
number.

2

e. A rental car costs $100 plus $0.25 for each mile traveled.
If Kaya pays $162.50 for the car, how many miles did she
travel?

250 miles

**HOMEWORK
ASSIGNMENT**

Page(s):

Exercises:

Solving Equations with Variables on Each Side

EXAMPLE Equations with Variables on Each Side

1 Solve $7x + 4 = 9x$.

$$7x + 4 = 9x$$ Write the equation.

$$7x - \boxed{7x} + 4 = 9x - \boxed{7x}$$ Subtract $\boxed{7x}$ from each side.

$$\boxed{4} = \boxed{2x}$$ Simplify by combining like terms.

$$\boxed{2} = \boxed{x}$$ Divide each side by $\boxed{2}$.

Your Turn Solve $3x + 6 = x$.

−3

EXAMPLE Equations with Variables on Each Side

FOLDABLES

ORGANIZE IT

Describe in your own words the steps to follow when you solve an equation with variables on both sides. Write an example of such an equation and solve it.

2 Solve $3x - 2 = 8x + 13$.

$$3x - 2 = 8x + 13$$ Write the equation.

$$3x - \boxed{8x} - 2 = 8x - \boxed{8x} + 13$$ Subtract $\boxed{8x}$ from each side.

$$-5x - 2 = 13$$ Simplify.

$$-5x - 2 + \boxed{2} = 13 + \boxed{2}$$ Add $\boxed{2}$ to each side

$$\boxed{-5x} = \boxed{15}$$ Simplify.

$$x = \boxed{-3}$$ Divide each side by $\boxed{-5}$.

Your Turn Solve $4x - 3 = 5x + 7$.

−10

EXAMPLE Use an Equation to Solve a Problem

3 Find the value of x so that the polygons have the same perimeter.

 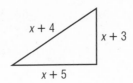

Triangle

$(\boxed{x+4}) + (\boxed{x+3}) + (\boxed{x+5}) = 3x + 12$

Rectangle

$(\boxed{x-2}) + (\boxed{x+4}) + (\boxed{x-2}) + (\boxed{x+4}) = 4x + 4$

Perimeter of Triangle = Perimeter of Rectangle

$3x + 12 \quad = \quad 4x + 4$

$3x - \boxed{3x} + 12 = 4x - \boxed{3x} + 4$

$12 = \boxed{x} + 4$

$12 - \boxed{4} = x + 4 - \boxed{4}$

$\boxed{8} = x$

Your Turn Find the value of x so that the polygons have the same perimeter.

2

HOMEWORK ASSIGNMENT

Page(s):

Exercises:

EXAMPLES Write Inequalities with < or >

Write an inequality for each sentence.

1 SPORTS Members of the little league team must be under 14 years old.

Let a = person's age.

a ⟨ < ⟩ 14

2 CONSTRUCTION The ladder must be over 30 feet tall to reach the top of the building.

Let h = ladder's height.

h ⟨ > ⟩ 30

Your Turn Write an inequality for each sentence.

a. Members of the peewee football team must be under 10 years old.

$a < 10$

b. The new building must be over 300 feet tall.

$h > 300$

EXAMPLES Write Inequalities with ≤ or ≥

Write an equality for each sentence.

3 POLITICS The president of the United States must be at least 35 years old.

Let a = president's age.

a ⟨ ≥ ⟩ 35

4 CAPACITY A theater can hold a maximum of 300 people.

Let p = theater's capacity.

p ⟨ ≤ ⟩ 300

© Glencoe/McGraw-Hill

Your Turn Write an inequality for each sentence.

a. To vote, you must be at least 18 years old.

$a \geq 18$

b. A football stadium can hold a maximum of 10,000 people.

$p \leq 10,000$

EXAMPLES Determine the Truth of an Inequality

For the given value, state whether the inequality is true or false.

5 $x - 4 < 6, x = 0$

$x - 4 < 6$	Write the inequality.
$\boxed{0} - 4 \overset{?}{<} 6$	Replace x with $\boxed{0}$.
$\boxed{-4} < 6$	Simplify.

Since $\boxed{-4}$ is less than $\boxed{6}$, $\boxed{-4} < \boxed{6}$ is $\boxed{\textbf{true}}$.

6 $3x \geq 4, x = 1$

$3x \geq 4$	Write the inequality.
$3\boxed{(1)} \overset{?}{\geq} 4$	Replace x with 1.
$\boxed{3} \ngeq 4$	Simplify.

Since $\boxed{3}$ is not greater than or equal to 4, the sentence

is $\boxed{\textbf{false}}$.

Your Turn For the given value, state whether the inequality is *true* or *false*.

a. $x - 5 < 8, x = 16$

false

b. $2x \geq 9, x = 5$

true

WRITE IT

Write in words what the symbols $<$, $>$, $\leq$, and $\geq$ mean.

_____

_____

_____

_____

EXAMPLES Graph an Inequality

Graph each inequality on a number line.

7 $n \leq -1$

Place a [**closed**] circle at -1. Then draw a line and an

arrow to the [**left**]. | The closed circle means the number -1 is included in the graph.

8 $n > -1$

Place an [**open**] circle at -1. Then draw a line and an arrow

to the [**right**]. | The open circle means -1 is *not* included in the graph.

Your Turn Graph each inequality on a number line.

a. $n \leq -3$

b. $n > -3$

HOMEWORK ASSIGNMENT

Page(s):

Exercises:

Solving Inequalities by Adding or Subtracting

WHAT YOU'LL LEARN

- Solve inequalities by using the Addition or Subtraction Properties of Inequality.

KEY CONCEPT

Addition and Subtraction Properties of Inequality. When you add or subtract the same number from each side of an inequality, the inequality remains true.

EXAMPLE Solve an Inequality Using Addition

1 Solve $n - 4 > 6$. Check your solution.

$$n - 4 > 6 \qquad \text{Write the inequality.}$$
$$n - 4 + \boxed{4} > 6 + \boxed{4} \qquad \text{Add } \boxed{4} \text{ to each side.}$$
$$n > \boxed{10} \qquad \text{Simplify.}$$

Check

$$n - 4 > 6 \qquad \text{Write the inequality.}$$
$$11 - 4 \overset{?}{>} 6 \qquad \text{Replace } n \text{ with a number}$$

$\boxed{\textbf{greater}}$ than 10, such as 11.

$$\boxed{7} > 6 ✔ \qquad \text{The statement is true.}$$

Any number greater than 10 will make the statement true, so the solution is $\boxed{\boldsymbol{n > 10}}$.

EXAMPLE Solve an Inequality Using Subtraction

2 Solve $x + 8 \le -7$. Check your solution.

$$x + 8 \le -7 \qquad \text{Write the inequality.}$$
$$x + 8 - \boxed{8} \le -7 - \boxed{8} \qquad \text{Subtract } \boxed{8} \text{ from each side.}$$
$$x \le \boxed{-15} \qquad \text{Simplify.}$$

Check Replace x in the original inequality with -15 and then with a number $\boxed{\textbf{less}}$ than -15.

$$x + 8 \le -7 \qquad\qquad x + 8 \le -7$$
$$-15 + 8 \le -7 \qquad\qquad -16 + 8 \le -7$$
$$\boxed{-7} \le -7 ✔ \qquad\qquad \boxed{-8} \le -7 ✔$$

The solution is $\boxed{\boldsymbol{x \le -15}}$.

Your Turn Solve each equation. Check your solution.

a. $n - 5 > 8$

$n > 13$

b. $x + 2 \leq -3$

$x \leq -5$

EXAMPLE Graph the Solution of an Inequality

3 Solve $s - \dfrac{3}{4} < 2$. Then graph the solution on a number line.

$$s - \frac{3}{4} < 2$$

$$s - \frac{3}{4} + \boxed{\frac{3}{4}} < 2 + \boxed{\frac{3}{4}}$$

$$s < \boxed{2\frac{3}{4}}$$

The solution is $s < \boxed{2\frac{3}{4}}$. Graph the solution.

Place an $\boxed{\text{open}}$ circle at $\boxed{2\frac{3}{4}}$. Draw a line and an arrow

to the $\boxed{\text{left}}$.

Your Turn Solve $s - \dfrac{1}{4} < 4$. Then graph the solution on a number line.

$s < 4\dfrac{1}{4}$

FOLDABLES

ORGANIZE IT

Write the main ideas, definitions and other notes as you learn how to solve inequalities by adding or subtracting. Be sure to include examples. Write your notes under the "Inequalities" tab.

EXAMPLE Use an Inequality to Solve a Problem

④ TOWING CAPACITY A pickup truck is towing a trailer that weighs 3,525 pounds. The maximum towing capacity of the truck is 4,700 pounds. Determine how much more weight can be added to the trailer and still be towed by the truck.

Words

The phrase *maximum capacity* means *less than or equal to*. So, the current weight being towed plus any more weight must be less than or equal to 4,700 pounds.

▼

Variable

Let w = more weight added.

▼

Equation

Current weight	plus	weight added	Must be less than or equal to	4,700 pounds
3,525	+	w	≤	4,700

$$3,525 + w \leq 4,700$$ Write the inequality.

$$3,525 - 3,525 + w \leq 4,700 - 3,525$$ Subtract **3,525** from each side.

$$w \leq 1,175$$ Simplify.

Up to **1,175** more pounds can be added to the trailer.

Your Turn A weightlifter can lift up to 375 pounds. He is currently lifting 255 pounds. Determine how much more weight can be added and still be lifted by the weightlifter.

Up to 120 more pounds can be added.

HOMEWORK ASSIGNMENT

Page(s):

Exercises:

Solving Inequalities by Multiplying or Dividing

WHAT YOU'LL LEARN

- Solve inequalities by using the Multiplication or Division Properties of Inequality.

KEY CONCEPT

Multiplication and Division By a Positive Number When you multiply or divide each side of an inequality by a positive number, the inequality remains true.

EXAMPLE Divide by a Positive Number

1 Solve $6x \leq -30$.

$$6x < -30$$ Write the inequality.

$$\frac{6x}{\boxed{6}} < \frac{-30}{\boxed{6}}$$ Divide each side by $\boxed{6}$.

$$x < \boxed{-5}$$ Simplify.

Your Turn Solve $4x < -24$.

$$x < -6$$

EXAMPLE Multiplying by a Positive Number

2 Solve $\frac{1}{2}p \geq 9$. Then graph the solution.

$$\frac{1}{2}p \geq 9$$ Write the inequality.

$$\boxed{2}\left(\frac{1}{2}p\right) \geq \boxed{2}(9)$$ Multiply each side by $\boxed{2}$.

$$p \geq \boxed{18}$$ Simplify.

Graph the solution, $p \geq \boxed{18}$.

Your Turn Solve $\frac{1}{2}p \geq 5$. Then graph the solution.

$$p \geq 10$$

© Glencoe/McGraw-Hill

EXAMPLES Multiply or Divide by a Negative Number

© Glencoe/McGraw-Hill

KEY CONCEPT

Multiplication and Division By a Negative Number When you multiply or divide each side of an inequality by a negative number, the direction of the inequality symbol must be reversed for the inequality to remain true.

3 Solve $\frac{b}{-4} \leq 5$.

$$\frac{b}{-4} \leq 5$$ Write the inequality.

$$\boxed{-4}\left(\frac{b}{-4}\right) \geq \boxed{-4}(5)$$ Multiply each side by $\boxed{-4}$ and reverse the inequality symbol.

$$b \geq \boxed{-20}$$ Simplify.

4 Solve $-4n > 60$. Then graph the solution.

$$-4n > -60$$ Write the inequality.

$$\frac{-4n}{\boxed{-4}} < \frac{-60}{\boxed{-4}}$$ Divide each side by $\boxed{-4}$ and reverse the inequality symbol.

$$n < \boxed{15}$$ Check this result.

Graph the solution, $n < \boxed{15}$.

Your Turn

a. Solve $\frac{n}{-2} \leq 7$.

$$n \geq -14$$

b. Solve $-3n \geq -18$. Then graph the solution.

$n < 6$

EXAMPLE Solve a Two-Step Inequality

5 PACKAGES A box weighs 1 pound. It is filled with books that weigh 2 pounds each. Jesse can carry at most 20 pounds. Assuming space is not an issue, write and solve an inequality to find how many books he can put in the box and still carry it.

The phrase *at most* means *less than or equal to*. Let $p =$ the number of books he puts in the box. Then write an inequality.

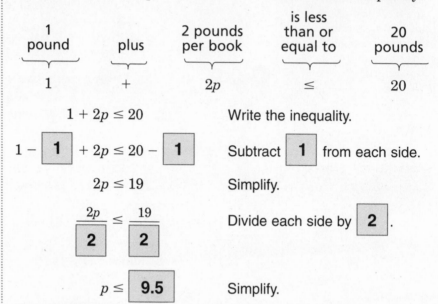

1 pound	plus	2 pounds per book	is less than or equal to	20 pounds
1	+	$2p$	≤	20

$1 + 2p \leq 20$ Write the inequality.

$1 - \boxed{1} + 2p \leq 20 - \boxed{1}$ Subtract $\boxed{1}$ from each side.

$2p \leq 19$ Simplify.

$\dfrac{2p}{\boxed{2}} \leq \dfrac{19}{\boxed{2}}$ Divide each side by $\boxed{2}$.

$p \leq \boxed{9.5}$ Simplify.

Since he cannot put half a book in the box, Jesse can put at

most $\boxed{9}$ books in the box.

Your Turn A box weighs 2 pounds. It is filled with toys that weigh 1 pound each. Danielle can carry at most 30 pounds. Assuming space is not an issue, write and solve an inequality to find how many toys she can put in the box and still carry it.

> **$2 + 1t \leq 30$; she can put at most 28 toys in the box**

HOMEWORK ASSIGNMENT

Page(s):

Exercises:

STUDY GUIDE

FOLDABLES™	VOCABULARY PUZZLEMAKER	*BUILD YOUR* VOCABULARY
Use your **Chapter 10 Foldable** to help you study for your chapter test.	To make a crossword puzzle, word search, or jumble puzzle of the vocabulary words in Chapter 10, go to: www.glencoe.com/sec/math/ t_resources/free/index.php	You can use your completed **Vocabulary Builder** *(page 252)* to help you solve the puzzle.

10-1
Simplifying Algebraic Expressions

1. Simplify the expression $3x - 4 - 8x + 2$ by writing the missing information:

   $\boxed{3x}$ and $\boxed{-8x}$ are like terms. $\boxed{-4}$ and $\boxed{2}$ are also like terms.

   $3x - 4 - 8x + 2 = 3x + \boxed{(-4)} - 8x + 2$ Definition of subtraction

   $= 3x + \boxed{(-8x)} + (-4) + 2$ Commutative Property

   $= \boxed{[3 + (-8)]} x + (-4) + 2$ Distributive Property

   $= \boxed{-5x - 2}$ Simplify

10-2
Solving Two-Step Equations

2. Define *two-step equation*.

A two-step equation is an equation that contains two operations.

What is the first step in solving each equation?

3. $3y - 2 = 16$ 4. $5 - 6x = -19$ 5. $32 = 4b + 6 - b$

Add 2 to each side.	**Subtract 5 from each side.**	**Add 4b and −b to combine like terms.**

10-3

Writing Two-Step Equations

Write each sentence as an algebraic equation.

6. Four less than six times a number is -40. $6n - 4 = -40$

7. The quotient of a number and 9, decreased by 3 is equal to 24.

$$\dfrac{n}{9} - 3 = 24$$

8. Jennifer bought 3 CD's, each having the same price. Her total for the purchase was \$51.84, which included \$3.84 in sales tax. Find the price of each CD.

Let p represent   **the price of a CD.**

Equation: Price of 3 CD's +   **sales tax**   =   **total purchase.**

$$\boxed{3p} + \boxed{3.84} = 51.84$$

$$3p + 3.84 - \boxed{3.84} = 51.84 - \boxed{3.84}$$

$$\boxed{3p} = \boxed{48}$$

$$\dfrac{\boxed{3p}}{3} = \dfrac{48}{3}$$

$$p = \boxed{16}$$

10-4

Frequency Tables

9. What is the first step in solving equations with variables on each side?

Sample Answer: Write an equivalent equation with the variables on one side.

Solve each equation.

10. $3x + 2 = 2x + 5$

3

11. $6x - 2 = 3x$

$\dfrac{2}{3}$

12. $7x - 2 = 9x + 6$

-4

© Glencoe/McGraw-Hill

10-5
Inequalities

Write an inequality for each sentence using the symbol <, >, ≤, or ≥.

13. Children under the age of 2 fly free. | $a < 2$

14. You must be at least 12 years old to go on the rocket ride.

$a \geq 12$

15. He can spend no more than \$15.00 for a gift. | $g \leq 15$

Write the solution shown by each graph.

16.

$n \leq 3$

17.

$n > -3$

10-6
Solving Inequalities by Adding or Subtracting

18. Explain what solving an inequality means.

Sample answer: finding all values for the variable that make the inequality true.

Solve each inequality.

19. $n - 6 < 21$

$n < 27$

20. $-10 \geq 7 + b$

$-17 \geq b \text{ or } b \leq -17$

10-7
Solving Inequalities by Multiplying or Dividing

21. Describe the conditions under which you reverse the direction of the inequality symbol when solving an inequality.

Reverse the direction of the inequality when multiplying or dividing each side by a negative number.

Solve each inequality.

22. $4c - 10 < -26$

$c < -4$

23. $\frac{d}{2} + 6 \leq -4$

$d \leq -20$

ARE YOU READY FOR THE CHAPTER TEST?

Math Online

Visit **msmath3.net** to access your textbook, more examples, self-check quizzes, and practice tests to help you study the concepts in Chapter 10.

Check the one that applies. Suggestions to help you study are given with each item.

☐ **I completed the review of all or most lessons without using my notes or asking for help.**

- You are probably ready for the Chapter Test.

- You may want to take the Chapter 10 Practice Test on page 507 of your textbook as a final check.

☐ **I used my Foldable or Study Notebook to complete the review of all or most lessons.**

- You should complete the Chapter 10 Study Guide and Review on pages 505–506 of your textbook.

- If you are unsure of any concepts or skills, refer back to the specific lesson(s).

- You may also want to take the Chapter 10 Practice Test on page 507.

☐ **I asked for help from someone else to complete the review of all or most lessons.**

- You should review the examples and concepts in your Study Notebook and Chapter 10 Foldable.

- Then complete the Chapter 10 Study Guide and Review on pages 505–506 of your textbook.

- If you are unsure of any concepts or skills, refer back to the specific lesson(s).

- You may also want to take the Chapter 10 Practice Test on page 507.

Student Signature	Parent/Guardian Signature

Teacher Signature

Algebra: Linear Functions

 Use the instructions below to make a Foldable to help you organize your notes as you study the chapter. You will see Foldable reminders in the margin of this Interactive Study Notebook to help you in taking notes.

Begin with a plain piece of notebook paper.

STEP 1 **Fold in Half**
Fold the paper lengthwise to the holes.

STEP 2 **Fold**
Fold the paper in fourths.

STEP 3 **Cut**
Open. Cut one side along the folds to make four tabs.

STEP 4 **Label**
Label each tab with the main topics as shown.

> Sequences and Functions
> Graphing Linear Functions
> Systems of Equations
> Graphing Linear Inequalities

 NOTE-TAKING TIP: When you begin studying a chapter in a textbook, first skim through the chapter to become familiar with the topics. As you skim, write questions about what you don't understand and what you'd like to know. Then, as you read the chapter, write answers to your questions.

Chapter 11

BUILD YOUR VOCABULARY

This is an alphabetical list of new vocabulary terms you will learn in Chapter 11. As you complete the study notes for the chapter, you will see Build Your Vocabulary reminders to complete each term's definition or description on these pages. Remember to add the textbook page number in the second column for reference when you study.

Vocabulary Term	Found on Page	Definition	Description or Example
arithmetic sequence [air-ith-MEH-tik]			
best-fit line			
boundary			
common difference			
common ratio			
dependent variable			
domain			
function			
function table			
geometric sequence [je-o-MET-rik]			
half plane			

Vocabulary Term	Found on Page	Definition	Description or Example
independent variable			
linear function			
range			
scatter plot			
sequence			
slope formula			
slope-intercept form			
substitution			
system of equations			
term			
x-intercept			
y-intercept			

Sequences

FOLDABLES

ORGANIZE IT

Under the "Sequences and Functions" tab of your Foldable, explain the difference between arithmetic and geometric sequences.

| Sequences and Functions |
| Graphing Linear Functions |
| Systems of Equations |
| Graphing Linear Inequalities |

BUILD YOUR VOCABULARY (pages 278–279)

A **sequence** is an $\boxed{\text{ordered list}}$ of numbers.

Each number in a $\boxed{\text{sequence}}$ is called a **term**.

An **arithmetic sequence** is a sequence in which the

$\boxed{\text{difference}}$ between any two consecutive terms is the same.

The difference between any two $\boxed{\text{consecutive}}$

$\boxed{\text{terms}}$ in an $\boxed{\text{arithmetic}}$ sequence is called the **common difference**.

EXAMPLE Identify Arithmetic Sequences

1 State whether the sequence 23, 15, 7, −1, −9 . . . is arithmetic. If it is, state the common difference. Write the next three terms of the sequence.

−3,　15,　7,　−1,　−9　Notice that 15 − 23 = −8,
　　　　　　　　　　　　　　 7 − 15 = −8, and so on.
−8　−8　−8　−8

The terms have a common $\boxed{\text{difference}}$ of −8, so the

sequence is $\boxed{\text{arithmetic}}$.

Continue the pattern to find the next three terms.

−9　$\boxed{-17}$,　$\boxed{-25}$,　$\boxed{-33}$

　　　−8　　−8　　−8

The next three terms are $\boxed{-17}$, $\boxed{-25}$, and $\boxed{-33}$.

Your Turn State whether the sequence 29, 27, 25, 23, 21, . . . is arithmetic. If it is, state the common difference. Write the next three terms of the sequence.

arithmetic; −2; 19, 17; 15

BUILD YOUR VOCABULARY (pages 278–279)

A **geometric sequence** is a sequence in which the

 quotient between any two consecutive terms is the same.

The quotient between any two **consecutive** terms

in a **geometric** sequence is called the **common ratio**.

EXAMPLES Identify Geometric Sequences

State whether each sequence is geometric. If it is, state the common ratio. Write the next three terms of the sequence.

2 −1, 3, −9, 27, −81, . . .

Notice that 3 ÷ (−1) = **−3** , −9 ÷ 3 = **−3** , and so on.

−1,   3,   −9,   27,   −81

× **(−3)** × **(−3)** × **(−3)** × **(−3)**

The terms have a common ratio of **−3** , so the sequence

is **geometric** .

Continue the pattern to find the next three terms.

−81   **243** ,   **−729** ,   **2,187**

× **(−3)** × **(−3)** × **(−3)**

The next three terms are **243** , **−729** , and **2,187** .

3 6, 12, 13, 26, 27, . . .

6,   12,   13,   26   27

×2   +1   ×2   +1

Since there is no | **common ratio** |, the sequence is

| **not geometric** | .

However, the sequence does have a pattern. Multiply the last

term by | **2** |, and then add | **1** | to get the next term.

27 | **54** |, | **55** |, | **110** |

×2   +1   ×2

The next three terms are | **54** |, | **55** |, and | **110** |.

Your Turn State whether each sequence is geometric. If it is, state the common ratio. Write the next three terms of the sequence.

a. 1, −2, 4, −8, 16, . . .

> **yes; −2; −32, 64, −128**

b. 1, 3, 7, 15, 31, . . .

> **not geometric; 63, 127, 255**

HOMEWORK ASSIGNMENT

Page(s):
Exercises:

WHAT YOU'LL LEARN

- Complete function tables.

A | **relationship** | where one thing | **depends upon** | another is called a **function**.

FOLDABLES

ORGANIZE IT

Under the "Sequences and Functions" tab of your Foldable, write how you would find the value of a function. You may wish to include an example.

EXAMPLES Find a Function Value

Find each function value.

1 $f(4)$ if $f(x) = x - 8$

$$f(x) = x - 8$$

$$f(\boxed{4}) = \boxed{4} - 8$$ Substitute $\boxed{4}$ for x into the function rule.

$$= \boxed{-4}$$ Simplify.

So, $f(4) = \boxed{-4}$.

2 $f(-6)$ if $f(x) = 3x + 4$

$$f(x) = 3x + 4$$

$$f(\boxed{-6}) = 3(\boxed{-6}) + 4$$ Substitute $\boxed{-6}$ for x into the function rule.

$$f(\boxed{-6}) = \boxed{-18} + 4$$ Multiply.

$$= \boxed{-14}$$ Simplify.

So, $f(-6) = \boxed{-14}$.

Your Turn Find each function value.

a. $f(2)$ if $f(x) = x - 7$

$$\boxed{-5}$$

b. $f(-2)$ if $f(x) = 2x + 6$

$$\boxed{2}$$

You can organize the [input], rule, and output of a function into a **function table**.

The variable for the [input] of a function is called the **independent variable**.

The variable for the [output] of a function is called the **dependent variable**.

The set of [input] values in a function is called the **domain**.

The set of [output] values in a function is called the **range**.

EXAMPLE Make a Function Table

③ Complete the function table for $f(x) = 4x - 1$.

Substitute each value of x, or [input], into the function rule.

Then simplify to find the [output].

Input x	Rule $4x - 1$	Output $f(x)$
−3		
−2		
−1		
0		
1		

$f(x) = 4x - 1$

$f(-3) =$ [4(−3) − 1] or [−13]

$f(-2) =$ [4(−2) − 1] or [−9]

$f(-1) =$ [4(−1) − 1] or [−5]

$f(0) =$ [4(0) − 1] or [−1]

$f(1) =$ [4(1) − 1] or [3]

Input x	Rule $4x - 1$	Output $f(x)$
−3	4(−3) − 1	−13
−2	4(−2) − 1	−9
−1	4(−1) − 1	−5
0	4(0) − 1	−1
1	4(1) − 1	3

Your Turn Complete the function table for $f(x) = 3x - 2$.

Input x	Rule $3x - 2$	Output $f(x)$
-3	$3(-3) - 2$	-11
-2	$3(-2) - 2$	-8
-1	$3(-1) - 2$	-5
0	$3(0) - 2$	-2
1	$3(1) - 2$	1

EXAMPLES Functions with Two Variables

PARKING FEES **The price for parking at a city lot is $3.00 plus $2.00 per hour.**

④ **Write a function using two variables to represent the price of parking for *h* hours.**

Words   Cost of parking equals $3.00 plus $2.00 per hour.

Function $p = $ **3** $+$ **2h**

The function $p = $ **3 + 2h** represents the situation.

⑤ **How much would it cost to park at the lot for 2 hours?**

Substitute **2** for h into the function rule.

$p = $ **3** $+$ **2h**

$p = 3 + 2$ **(2)** or **7**

It will cost **$7.00** to park for 2 hours.

Your Turn **TAXI** **The price of a taxi ride is $5.00 plus $4.00 per hour.**

a. Write a function using two variables to represent the price of riding a taxi for *h* hours.

$p = 5 + 4h$

b. How much would it cost for a 3-hour taxi ride?

$17.00

HOMEWORK ASSIGNMENT

Page(s):

Exercises:

Graphing Linear Functions

Graph a Function

WHAT YOU'LL LEARN

• Graph linear functions by using function tables and plotting points.

FOLDABLES

ORGANIZE IT

Under the "Graphing Linear Functions" tab of your Foldable, include a linear function and its graph.

1 **Graph $y = x - 3$.**

Step 1 Choose some values for x. Make a function table. Include a column of ordered pairs of the form (x, y).

x	$x - 3$	y	(x, y)
0	**0** $- 3$	**−3**	**(0, −3)**
1	**1** $- 3$	**−2**	**(1, −2)**
2	**2** $- 3$	**−1**	**(2, −1)**
3	**3** $- 3$	**0**	**(3, 0)**

Step 2 Graph each ordered pair.

Draw a line that passes through each point. Note that the ordered pair for any point on this line is a solution of $y = x - 3$. The line is the complete graph of the function.

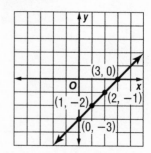

Check It appears from the graph that $(-1, -4)$ is also a solution. Check this by substitution.

$y = x - 3$ Write the function.

−4 $\overset{?}{=}$ **−1** $- 3$ Replace x and y.

−4 $=$ **−4**   Simplify.

Your Turn Graph $y = x - 2$.

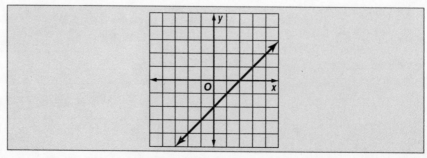

BUILD YOUR VOCABULARY (pages 278–279)

A function in which the graph of solutions forms a

| line | is called a linear function.

The value of x where the graph crosses the | **x-axis** | is called the **x-intercept.**

The value of y where the graph crosses the | **y-axis** | is called the **y-intercept.**

EXAMPLE Use x- and y-intercepts

2 Which graph represents $y = 2x + 1$?

a.

b.

c.

d.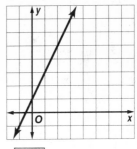

The graph will cross the x-axis when $y = $ | 0 |.

| 0 | $ = 2x + 1$ Replace y with | 0 |.

| −1 | $=$ | 2x | Subtract | 1 |. Then simplify.

| $-\dfrac{1}{2}$ | $= x$ Divide by | 1 |. Then simplify.

The graph will cross the y-axis when $x = \boxed{0}$.

$y = 2 \boxed{(0)} + 1$ Replace x with $\boxed{0}$.

$y = \boxed{1}$ Simplify.

The x-intercept is $\boxed{-\dfrac{1}{2}}$ and the y-intercept is $\boxed{1}$.

Graph $\boxed{D}$ is the only graph with both of these intercepts.

Your Turn   Which graph represents $y = 3x + 3$?

a.

b.

c.

d.
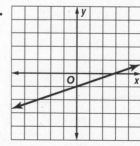

C

HOMEWORK ASSIGNMENT

Page(s): _____

Exercises: _____

The Slope Formula

WHAT YOU'LL LEARN

- Find the slope of a line using the slope formula.

KEY CONCEPTS

Slope Formula The slope m of a line passing through points (x_1, y_1) and (x_2, y_2) is the ratio of the difference in the y-coordinates to the corresponding difference in the x-coordinates.

EXAMPLE Positive Slope

1 Find the slope of the line that passes through $A(3, 3)$ and $B(2, 0)$.

$m = \dfrac{y_2 - y_1}{x_2 - x_1}$ Definition of slope

$m = \dfrac{0 - 3}{2 - 3}$ $(x_1, y_1) = (3, 3)$
                $(x_2, y_2) = (2, 0)$

$m = \dfrac{3}{1}$ or 3   Simplify.

EXAMPLE Negative Slope

2 Find the slope of the line that passes through $X(-2, 3)$ and $Y(3, 0)$.

$m = \dfrac{y_2 - y_1}{x_2 - x_1}$ Definition of slope

$m = \dfrac{\boxed{0 - 3}}{\boxed{3 - (-2)}}$ $(x_1, y_1) = (-2, 3),$

                $(x_2, y_2) = (3, 0)$

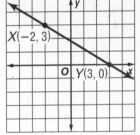

$m = \dfrac{-3}{5}$ or $-\dfrac{3}{5}$ Simplify.

EXAMPLE Zero Slope

3 Find the slope of the line that passes through $P(6, 5)$ and $Q(2, 5)$.

$m = \dfrac{y_2 - y_1}{x_2 - x_1}$ Definition of slope

$m = \dfrac{\boxed{5 - 5}}{\boxed{2 - 6}}$ $(x_1, y_1) = (6, 5),$

                $(x_2, y_2) = (2, 5)$

$m = \dfrac{0}{-4}$ or 0   Simplify.

The slope is 0. The slope of any horizontal line is $\boxed{0}$.

Mathematics: Applications and Concepts, Course 3   **289**

EXAMPLE Undefined Slope

④ **Find the slope of the line that passes through each pair of points.**

$m = \dfrac{y_2 - y_1}{x_2 - x_1}$ Definition of slope

$m = \dfrac{\boxed{6 - 4}}{\boxed{2 - 2}}$ $(x_1, y_1) = (2, 4),$

                            $(x_2, y_2) = (2, 6)$

$m = \dfrac{2}{0}$ Simplify.

Division by 0 is not defined. So, the slope is undefined. The

slope of any   **vertical**   line is undefined.

Your Turn Find the slope of the line that passes through each pair of points.

a. $A(4, 3)$, $B(1, 0)$

> 1

b. $X(-3, 3)$, $Y(1, 0)$

> $-\dfrac{3}{4}$

c. $P(1, 6)$, $Q(2, 6)$

> 0

d. $G(-2, 1)$, $H(-2, 0)$

> **undefined**

HOMEWORK ASSIGNMENT

Page(s):

Exercises:

Slope-Intercept Form

WHAT YOU'LL LEARN

- Graph linear equations using the slope and y-intercept.

BUILD YOUR VOCABULARY (page 279)

Slope-intercept form is when an equation is written in the form $\boxed{y = mx + b}$, where m is the $\boxed{\textbf{slope}}$ and b is the $\boxed{\textbf{y-intercept}}$.

EXAMPLES Find the Slopes and y-intercepts of Graphs

State the slope and the y-intercept of the graph of each equation.

1 $y = \frac{3}{4}x - 5$

$y = \frac{3}{4}x + \left(\boxed{-5}\right)$ Write the equation in the form $y = mx + b$.

$y = mx \ + \ b \qquad m = \frac{3}{4} \ \ b = \boxed{-5}$

The slope of the graph is $\boxed{\dfrac{3}{4}}$, and the y-intercept is $\boxed{-5}$.

2 $2x + y = 8$

$2x + y = 8$ Write the original equation.

$-\boxed{2x} \quad -\boxed{2x}$ Subtract $\boxed{2x}$ from each side.

$y = \boxed{8 - 2x}$ Simplify.

$y = \boxed{-2x + 8}$ Write the equation in the form $y = mx + b$.

$y = \ mx + b \qquad m = \boxed{-2}, b = \boxed{8}$

The slope of the graph is $\boxed{-2}$ and the y-intercept is $\boxed{8}$.

Your Turn State the slope and the y-intercept of the graph of each equation.

a. $y = \frac{1}{4}x - 2$

slope = $\frac{1}{4}$;
y-intercept = -2

b. $3x + y = 5$

slope = -3;
y-intercept = 5

EXAMPLE Graph an Equation

3 Graph $y = \frac{2}{3}x + 2$ using the slope and y-intercept.

Step 1 Find the slope and y-intercept.

$$y = \frac{2}{3}x + 2$$

slope $= \frac{2}{3}$

y-intercept $= 2$

Step 2 Graph the y-intercept (0, 2).

Step 3 Use the slope to locate a second point on the line.

$m = \frac{2}{3}$

change in y:
up 2 units

change in x:
right 3 units

Step 4 Draw a line through the two points.

Your Turn Graph $y = \frac{1}{3}x + 3$ using the slope and y-intercept.

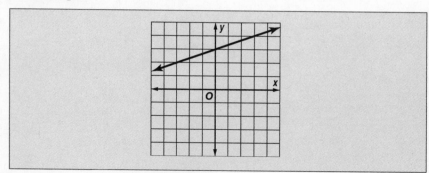

WHAT YOU'LL LEARN

• Construct and interpret scatter plots.

BUILD YOUR VOCABULARY (pages 278–279)

A **scatter plot** is a graph that shows the | **relationship** | between | **two** | sets of data.

A **best-fit line** is a line that is very close to | **most** | of the data points in a scatter plot.

EXAMPLES Identify a Relationship

Determine whether a scatter plot of the data for the following might show a *positive*, *negative*, or *no relationship*.

① cups of hot chocolate sold at a concession stand and the outside temperature

As the temperature decreases, the number of cups of hot

chocolate sold | **increases** |. Therefore, the scatter plot

might show a | **negative** | relationship.

② birthday and number of sports played

The number of sports played does not depend on your

birthday. Therefore, the scatter plot shows | **no** | relationship.

Your Turn Determine whether a scatter plot of the data for the following might show a *positive*, *negative*, or *no relationship*.

a. number of cups of lemonade sold at a concession stand and the outside temperature

| **positive** |

b. age and the color of your hair

| **no relationship** |

EXAMPLES Draw a Best-Fit Line

GROWTH A boy's heights, measured from age 2 to age 9, are given.

Age (years)	Height (cm)
2	88
3	92
4	103
5	106
6	107
7	121
8	125
9	136

❸ **Make a scatter plot using the data. Then draw a line that seems to best represent the data.**

Graph each of the data points.

Draw a ⬛ **line** that best fits the data.

Boy's Height, Ages 2 Through 9

❹ **Write an equation for the best-fit line.**

The line passes through the points at (4, 103) and (6, 117). Use these points to find the slope of the line.

$$m = \frac{y_2 - y_1}{x_2 - x_1}$$ Definition of slope

$$m = \frac{\boxed{117 - 103}}{\boxed{6 - 4}}$$ $(x_1, y_1) = (15, 40), (x_2, y_2) = (6, 117)$

$$m = \frac{\boxed{14}}{\boxed{2}} \text{ or } \boxed{7}$$ Simplify.

The slope is $\boxed{7}$ and the y-intercept is $\boxed{70}$.

Use the slope and the *y*-intercept to write the equation.

$y = mx + b$ Slope-intercept form

$y = \boxed{7} c + \boxed{70}$ $m = \boxed{7}$, $b = \boxed{70}$

The equation for the best-fit line is $\boxed{y = 7x + 70}$.

5 **Use the equation to predict the boy's height at age 11.**

$y = 7x + 70$ Equation for the best-fit line

$y = 7(11) + 70$ or $\boxed{147}$

At age 11, the boy's height is about $\boxed{147}$ centimeters.

Your Turn The table shows the average hourly earnings of U.S. production workers since 1995.

a. Make a scatter plot using the data.

b. Write an equation for the best-fit line using points (0, 11.43) and (5, 13.76).

c. Use the equation to predict the average hourly earnings of U.S. production workers in 2004.

U.S. Production Workers Earnings	
Year Since 1995	Average Hourly Earnings
0	$11.43
1	$11.82
2	$12.28
3	$12.78
4	$13.24
5	$13.76
6	$14.32

Source: *The World Almanac*

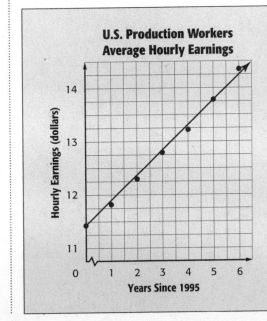

**U.S. Production Workers
Average Hourly Earnings**

$y = 0.466x + 11.43$;
$15.62

Years Since 1995

Hourly Earnings (dollars)

Graphing Systems of Equations

WHAT YOU'LL LEARN

• Solve systems of linear equations by graphing.

BUILD YOUR VOCABULARY (pages 278–279)

A [**set**] of two or more equations [**considered**]

[**together**] is called a **system of equations**.

ORGANIZE IT

Under the "Systems of Equations" tab of your Foldable, explain how you know whether a system of equations has one solution, infinitely many solutions, or no solution.

EXAMPLE One Solution

1 Solve the system $y = x - 1$ and $y = 2x - 2$ by graphing.

The graphs of the equations

appear to intersect at [**(1, 0)**].
Check this estimate.

Check $y = x - 1$ ⠀⠀⠀⠀⠀⠀⠀⠀⠀ $y = 2x - 2$

[0] $\overset{?}{=} 1 -$ [1] ⠀⠀⠀⠀⠀⠀ [0] $\overset{?}{=} 2$ [(1)] $- 2$

[0] $=$ [0] ⠀⠀⠀⠀⠀⠀⠀⠀⠀⠀ [0] $=$ [0]

The solution is [**(1, 0)**].

Your Turn Solve the system $y = x + 3$ and $y = 3x - 3$ by graphing.

(3, 6)

EXAMPLE Infinitely Many Solutions

2 Solve the system $y = \frac{1}{2}x + 3$ and $y - \frac{1}{2}x = 3$ by graphing.

Write $y - \frac{1}{2}x = 3$ in slope-intercept form.

$$y - \frac{1}{2}x = 3 \qquad \text{Write the equation.}$$

$$y - \frac{1}{2}x + \boxed{\frac{1}{2}x} = 3 + \boxed{\frac{1}{2}x} \qquad \text{Add } \boxed{\frac{1}{2}x} \text{ to each side.}$$

$$y = \boxed{\frac{1}{2}x + 3} \qquad \text{Both equations are the same.}$$

The solution is $\boxed{\textbf{all}}$ the coordinates of points on the graph of $y = \frac{1}{2}x + 3$.

Your Turn Solve the system $y = 2x + 4$ and $y - 2x = 4$ by graphing.

The solution of the system is all the coordinates of the points on the graph of $y = 2x + 4$.

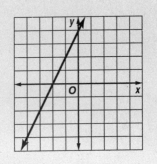

EXAMPLE No Solution

3 **PHONE RATES** One phone company charges $3 a month plus 10 cents a minute for long-distance calls. Another company charges $5 a month plus 10 cents a minute for long-distance calls. For how many minutes will the total monthly charges of the two companies be the same?

Let x equal the number of minutes.

Let y equal the total monthly cost.

Write an equation to represent each company's charge for long-distance phone calls.

1st company: $y = \boxed{0.10x + 3}$

2nd company: $y = \boxed{0.10x + 5}$

Graph the system of equations.

$y = 0.10x + 3$

$y = 0.10x + 5$

The graphs appear to be

| parallel | lines.

Since there is no coordinate pair that is a solution of both

equations, there is | no | solution of this system of

equations.

For | any | amount of minutes, the first company will

charge less than the second company.

Your Turn One phone company charges $20 a month plus
15 cents a minute for long-distance calls. Another company
charges $25 a month plus 15 cents a minute for long-distance
calls. For how many minutes will the total monthly charges of
the two companies be the same?

**For any amount of minutes, the first
company will charge less than the second
company.**

BUILD YOUR VOCABULARY (pages 278–279)

A more accurate way to solve a system of | **equations**

than by graphing, is by using a method called **substitution**.

EXAMPLE Solve by Substitution

④ **Solve the system $y = 3x - 4$ and $y = 5$ by substitution.**

Since y must have the | same | value in both equations, you

can replace y with | 5 | in the first equation.

| $y = 3x - 4$ | Write the first equation. |

| 5 | $= 3x - 4$ Replace y with | 5 |.

$5 +$ | 4 | $= 3x - 4 +$ | 4 | Add | 4 | to each side.

| 9 | $= 3x$ Simplify.

$\dfrac{9}{\boxed{3}} = \dfrac{3x}{\boxed{3}}$ Divide each side by | 3 |.

| 3 | $= x$ Simplify.

The solution of this system of equations

is | (3, 5) |. You can check the solution

by graphing. The graphs appear to

intersect at | (3, 5) |, so the solution is

correct.

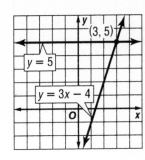

Your Turn Solve the system $y = 2x - 3$ and $y = 3$ by substitution.

(3, 3)

HOMEWORK ASSIGNMENT

Page(s): _____

Exercises: _____

_____

_____

Graphing Linear Inequalities

WHAT YOU'LL LEARN

• Graph linear inequalities.

BUILD YOUR VOCABULARY (pages 278–279)

The line which separates the $\boxed{\text{solutions}}$ from the

points that are $\boxed{\text{not}}$ solutions in the graph of a

$\boxed{\text{linear}}$ inequality is called the **boundary**.

The $\boxed{\text{region}}$ which contains the $\boxed{\text{solutions}}$ in

the graph of a linear inequality is called the **half plane**.

FOLDABLES

ORGANIZE IT

Under the "Graphing Linear Inequalities" tab of your Foldable, explain how to graph an inequality.

Sequences and Functions
Graphing Linear Functions
Systems of Equations
Graphing Linear Inequalities

EXAMPLE   Graph an Inequality

1 Graph $y \leq -x + 3$.

Step 1   Graph the boundary line $y = -x + 3$. Since $\leq$ is used in the inequality, make the

boundary line a $\boxed{\text{solid}}$ line.

Step 2   Test a point not on the boundary line, such as (0, 0).

$$y \overset{?}{\leq} x + 3 \qquad \text{Write the inequality.}$$

$$\boxed{0} \leq -\left(\boxed{0}\right) + 3 \qquad \text{Replace } x \text{ and } y.$$

$$0 \leq \boxed{3} \checkmark \qquad \text{Simplify.}$$

Step 3   Since (0, 0) is a solution of $y = -x + 3$, shade the

region that contains $\boxed{(0, 0)}$.

Your Turn Graph $y \leq 2x - 2$.

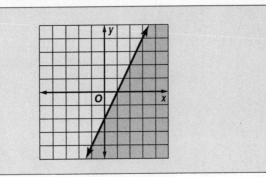

EXAMPLE Graph an Inequality to Solve a Problem

2 **CRAFTS** Sylvia is making items to sell at the school craft sale. Each flower basket takes 15 minutes, and each flower pin takes 1 minute to make. She can spend, at most, 60 minutes making crafts one afternoon. Graph the inequality showing the possible numbers of each item she can make that afternoon.

Let x represent the number of flower baskets and y represent the number of flower pins. Write the inequality $15x + 1y \leq 60$.

The related equation is $15x + y = 60$.

$15x + y = 60$	Write the equation.
$15x + y - 15x = 60 - 15x$	Subtract $15x$ from each side.
$y = \boxed{-15x + 60}$	Slope-intercept form

Graph $y = -15x + 60$. Test $(0, 0)$ in the original inequality.

$15x + 1y \leq 60$	Write the inequality.
$15\left(\boxed{0}\right) + 1\left(\boxed{0}\right) \stackrel{?}{\leq} 60$	Replace x and y with $\boxed{0}$.
$\boxed{0} \leq 60$	Simplify.

Since Sylvia cannot make a negative number or a fractional number of flower baskets or flower pins, the answer is any pair of integers represented in the shaded region. For example, she could make 1 basket and 30 pins.

Your Turn Josef is baking items to sell at the school bake sale. Each cake takes 40 minutes, and each pre-made brownie takes 1 minute to unwrap. He can spend, at most, 120 minutes baking one afternoon. Graph the inequality showing the possible numbers of each item he can make that afternoon.

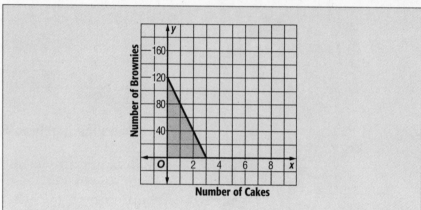

BRINGING IT ALL TOGETHER

STUDY GUIDE

FOLDABLES	VOCABULARY PUZZLEMAKER	*BUILD YOUR VOCABULARY*
Use your **Chapter 11 Foldable** to help you study for your chapter test.	To make a crossword puzzle, word search, or jumble puzzle of the vocabulary words in Chapter 11, go to: www.glencoe.com/sec/math/ t_resources/free/index.php	You can use your completed **Vocabulary Builder** *(pages 278–279)* to help you solve the puzzle.

11–1
Sequences

State whether each sequence is *arithmetic*, *geometric*, or *neither*. If it is arithmetic or geometric, state the common difference or common ratio. Write the next three terms of each sequence.

1. 14, 19, 24, 29, 34, . . .   **2.** 2, 0, −3, −7, −12, . . .   **3.** −1. 3, −9, 18, −54, . . .

| arithmetic; 5; 39, 44, 49 | neither; −18, −25, −33 | geometric; −3; 162, −486, 1,458 |

11–2
Functions

Match each description with the word it describes.

a. independent variable
b. dependent variable
c. domain
d. range

4. an output value of a function **b**

5. the set of values of the dependent variable **d**

6. the underlined letter in $f(x) = 2\underline{x} + 5$ **a**

7. Complete the function table for $f(x) = 2x + 2$. Then give the domain and range.

Domain: **[−2, 0, 1, 3]**

Range: **[0, 2, 4, 8]**

x	$2x + 2$	$f(x)$
−2	**2(−2) + 2**	**0**
0	**2(0) + 2**	**2**
1	**2(1) + 2**	**4**
3	**2(3) + 2**	**8**

11–3

Graphing Linear Functions

8. Complete the function table. Then graph $y = -x + 2$.

x	$-x + 2$	y	(x, y)
-2	**2 + 2**	**4**	**(−2, 4)**
0	**0 + 2**	**2**	**(0, 2)**
2	**−2 + 2**	**0**	**(2, 0)**
3	**−3 + 2**	**−1**	**(3, −1)**

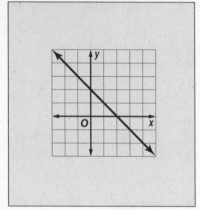

9. Explain how to find the *x*-intercept of the graph of a linear function. Then find the *x*-intercept of $y = 2x + 8$.

   Replace *y* with 0 and solve for *x*; −4.

10. Explain how to find the *y*-intercept of the graph of a linear function. Then find the *y*-intercept of $y = 2x + 8$.

    Replace *x* with 0 and solve for *y*; 8.

11–4

The Slope Formula

Find the slope of the line that passes through each pair of points.

11. $A(1, -2), B(4, 4)$ 12. $C(1, 2), D(3, -2)$ 13. $E(-1, 2), F(2, 2)$

    $\dfrac{1}{2}$ -2 0

11–5

Slope-Intercept Form

State the slope and the *y*-intercept for the graph of each equation.

14. $y = -3x + 4$ 15. $y = \dfrac{2}{3}x - 7$ 16. $\dfrac{1}{2}x + y = 8$

| slope = $\dfrac{2}{3}$; *y*-intercept = −7 | slope = −3; *y*-intercept = 4 | slope = $\dfrac{1}{2}$; *y*-intercept = 8 |

11–6
Scatter Plots

17. Complete. A scatter plot that shows a negative relationship will have a pattern of data points that go | **downward to the right** | .

Write whether a scatter plot of the data for the following might show a *positive*, *negative*, or *no relationship*.

18. favorite color and type of pet

| **no relationship** |

19. the amount of rain and the water level of a pond

| **positive relationship** |

11–7
Graphing Systems of Equations

Solve each system of equations by substitution.

20. $y = -3x + 2$
$y = -1$

| **(1, −1)** |

21. $y = x + 5$
$y = x + 7$

| **no solution** |

22. $y = 4x + 1$
$y = -x + 6$

| **(1, 5)** |

11–8
Graphing Linear Inequalities

Write *true* or *false* beside each statement. If the statement is false, write the correct words in place of the underlined words.

23. The non-shaded region contains all the solutions of the inequality. | **false; shaded** |

24. A dashed boundary line means that points on the line are solutions of the inequality. | **false; solid** |

25. If the inequality uses the symbol $<$ or $>$, the boundary line will be a solid line. | **false; $\leq$ or $\geq$** |

CHAPTER 11 Checklist

ARE YOU READY FOR THE CHAPTER TEST?

Math Online

Visit **msmath3.net** to access your textbook, more examples, self-check quizzes, and practice tests to help you study the concepts in Chapter 11.

Check the one that applies. Suggestions to help you study are given with each item.

☐ **I completed the review of all or most lessons without using my notes or asking for help.**

- You are probably ready for the Chapter Test.
- You may want to take the Chapter 11 Practice Test on page 555 of you textbook as a final check.

☐ **I used my Foldable or Study Notebook to complete the review of all or most lessons.**

- You should complete the Chapter 11 Study Guide and Review on pages 552–554 of your textbook.
- If you are unsure of any concepts or skills, refer to the specific lesson(s).
- You may also want to take the Chapter 11 Practice Test on page 555.

☐ **I asked for help from someone else to complete the review of all or most lessons.**

- You should review the examples and concepts in your Study Notebook and Chapter 11 Foldable.
- Then complete the Chapter 11 Study Guide and Review on pages 552–554 of your textbook.
- If you are unsure of any concepts or skills, refer to the specific lesson(s).
- You may also want to take the Chapter 11 Practice Test on page 555.

Student Signature

Parent/Guardian Signature

Teacher Signature

Algebra: Nonlinear Functions and Polynomials

 Use the instructions below to make a Foldable to help you organize your notes as you study the chapter. You will see Foldable reminders in the margin of this Interactive Study Notebook to help you in taking notes.

Begin with 7 sheets of $8\frac{1}{2}$" × 11" paper.

STEP 1 **Fold and Cut**
Fold a sheet of paper in half lengthwise. Cut a 1" tab along the left edge through one thickness.

STEP 2 **Glue and Label**
Glue the 1" tab down. Write the title of the lesson on the front tab.

Linear & Nonlinear Functions

STEP 3 **Repeat and Staple**
Repeat Steps 1–2 for the remaining sheets of paper. Staple together to form a booklet.

Linear & Nonlinear Functions

 NOTE-TAKING TIP: When you take notes, define new terms and write about the new concepts you are learning in your own words. Write your own examples that use the new terms and concepts.

BUILD YOUR VOCABULARY

This is an alphabetical list of new vocabulary terms you will learn in Chapter 12. As you complete the study notes for the chapter, you will see Build Your Vocabulary reminders to complete each term's definition or description on these pages. Remember to add the textbook page number in the second column for reference when you study.

Vocabulary Term	Found on Page	Definition	Description or Example
monomial			
nonlinear function			
polynomial			
quadratic function			

Linear and Nonlinear Functions

WHAT YOU'LL LEARN

- Determine whether a function is linear or nonlinear.

FOLDABLES

ORGANIZE IT

Explain how to identify linear and nonlinear functions using graphs, equations, and tables on the Lesson 12-1 section of your Foldable journal.

> Linear & Nonlinear Functions

BUILD YOUR VOCABULARY (page 308)

Nonlinear functions do not have [**constant**] rates of change. Therefore, their graphs are not straight lines.

EXAMPLES Identify Functions Using Graphs

Determine whether each graph represents a *linear* or *nonlinear* function. Explain.

1

The graph is a curve, not a straight line. So it represents a

[**nonlinear**] function.

2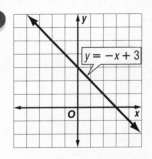

The graph is a straight line. So it represents a

[**linear**] function.

Your Turn Determine whether each graph represents a *linear* or *nonlinear* function. Explain.

a.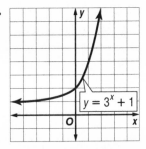

Nonlinear; the graph is a curve.

b.

Linear; the graph is a straight line.

EXAMPLES Identify Functions Using Equations

Determine whether each equation represents a *linear* or *nonlinear* function. Explain.

3 $y = 5x^2 + 3$

Since x is raised to the [**second**] power, the equation

cannot be written in the form $y = mx + b$. So, this function

is [**nonlinear**].

4 $y - 4 = 5x$

Rewrite the equation as $y = $ [**5x + 4**]. This equation is

[**linear**] since it is of the form $y = mx + b$.

Your Turn Determine whether each equation represents a *linear* or *nonlinear* function. Explain.

a. $y = x^2 - 1$

Nonlinear; the power of *x* is greater than one.

b. $y = x$

Linear; the equation can be written as $y = 1x + 0$.

EXAMPLES Identify Functions Using Tables

Determine whether each table represents a *linear* or *nonlinear* function. Explain.

5

x	2	4	6	8
y	2	20	54	104

As x increases by [**2**], y increases by a greater amount each

time. The rate of change is not [**constant**], so this function

is [**nonlinear**].

6

As *x* increases by **3**, *y* increases by **9** each time. The

rate of change is **constant**, so this function is **linear**.

Your Turn Determine whether each table represents a *linear* or *nonlinear* function. Explain.

a.

x	1	3	5	7
y	3	7	11	15

Linear; the rate of change is constant, as *x* increases by 2, *y* increases by 4.

b.

x	1	2	3	4
y	1	8	27	64

Nonlinear; the rate of change is not constant.

HOMEWORK ASSIGNMENT

Page(s):
Exercises:

Graphing Quadratic Functions

WHAT YOU'LL LEARN

- Graph quadratic functions.

BUILD YOUR VOCABULARY (page 308)

A **quadratic function** is a function in which the | greatest |

power of the | variable | is | 2 |.

EXAMPLES Graph Quadratic Functions: $y = ax^2$

① Graph $y = 5x^2$.

To graph a linear function, make a table of values, plot the ordered pairs, and connect the points with a smooth curve.

x	$5x^2$	y	(x, y)
−2	$5(-2)^2 =$ **20**	**20**	(−2, **20**)
−1	$5(-1)^2 =$ **5**	**5**	(−1, **5**)
0	$5(0)^2 =$ **0**	**0**	(0, **0**)
1	$5(1)^2 =$ **5**	**5**	(1, **5**)
2	$5(2)^2 =$ **20**	**20**	(2, **20**)

FOLDABLES

ORGANIZE IT

Record what you learn about graphing quadratic functions and using the graphs to solve problems on the Lesson 12-2 section of your Foldable.

Linear & Nonlinear Functions

Your Turn Graph $y = -3x^2$.

Sample table: $-3x^2$

x	$-3x^2$	y	(x, y)
−2	$-3(-2)^2 = -12$	−12	(−2, −12)
−1	$-3(-1)^2 = -3$	−3	(−1, −3)
0	$-3(0)^2 = 0$	0	(0, 0)
1	$-3(1)^2 = -3$	−3	(1, −3)
2	$-3(2)^2 = -12$	−12	(2, −12)

EXAMPLE Graph Quadratic Functions: $y = ax^2 + c$

2 Graph $y = 3x^2 + 1$.   (parallels Example 3 in text)

x	$3x^2 + 1$	y	(x, y)
−2	$3(-2)^2 + 1 =$ **13**	**13**	(−2, **13**)
−1	$3(-1)^2 + 1 = 4$	4	(−1, 4)
0	$3(0)^2 + 1 =$ **1**	**1**	(0, **1**)
1	$3(1)^2 + 1 = 4$	4	(1, 4)
2	$3(2)^2 + 1 = 13$	13	(2, 13)

Your Turn Graph $y = -2x^2 - 1$.

Sample table:

x	$-2x^2 - 1$	y	(x, y)
−2	$-2(-2)^2 - 1 = -9$	−9	(−2, −9)
−1	$-2(-1)^2 - 1 = -3$	−3	(−1, −3)
0	$-2(0)^2 - 1 = -1$	−1	(0, −1)
1	$-2(1)^2 - 1 = -3$	−3	(1, −3)
2	$-2(2)^2 - 1 = -9$	−9	(2, −9)

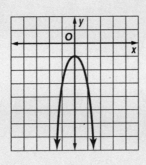

HOMEWORK ASSIGNMENT

Page(s):

Exercises:

Simplifying Polynomials

WHAT YOU'LL LEARN

• Simplify polynomials.

BUILD YOUR VOCABULARY (page 308)

A **monomial** is a number, a variable, or a **product** of a number and one or more variables.

An algebraic expression that is the **sum** or **difference** of one or more **monomials** is called a **polynomial**.

EXAMPLE Simplify Polynomials

1 Simplify $3r + 8p - 6q - r$.

The like terms in this expression are **$3r$** and **$-r$**.

$3r + 8p - 6q - r$ Write the polynomial.

$= 3r + 8p - 6q + \boxed{(-r)}$ Definition of subtraction

$= [3r + (-r)] + 8p - 6q$ Group **like terms**.

$= \boxed{2r} + 8p - 6q$ Simplify by combining like terms.

2 Simplify $-6x^2 + 14 + 3x$.

There are no like terms in the expression.

Therefore, $-6x^2 + 14 + 3x$ is in **simplest** form.

Your Turn Simplify each polynomial. If the polynomial cannot be simplified, write *simplest form*.

a. $2r + 7p - 3q - 5r$

$-3r + 7p - 3q$

b. $-2x^2 + 4 + x$

simplest form

FOLDABLES

ORGANIZE IT

In the Lesson 12-3 section of your Foldable, include an example of a polynomial that needs to be simplified. Then explain how to simplify the polynomial.

Linear & Nonlinear Functions

---

3 Simplify $2x + 8x^2 - 9x + 3 - 2x^2$.

$2x + 8x^2 - 9x + 3 - 2x^2$ is equal to $2x + 8x^2 +$ $\boxed{(-9x)}$ $+$ $3 +$ $\boxed{(-2x^2)}$.

Write the polynomial. Then group and add $\boxed{\textbf{like}}$ terms.

$2x + 8x^2 + (-9x) + 3 + (-2x^2)$

$= [8x^2 + \boxed{-2x^2}] + [2x + (\boxed{-9x})] + 3$

$= \boxed{6x^2} + (\boxed{-7x}) + 3$

$= \boxed{6x^2} - 7x + 3$

Thus, $2x + 8x^2 - 9x + 3 - 2x^2 =$ $\boxed{6x^2 - 7x + 3}$.

REMEMBER IT

To be consistent, write the results of simplifying polynomials in standard form, with the powers of the variable decreasing from left to right.

Your Turn Simplify $3x + 2x^2 - 6x + 2 - 3x^2$.

$-x^2 - 3x + 2$

HOMEWORK ASSIGNMENT

Page(s):

Exercises:

Adding Polynomials

EXAMPLES **Add Polynomials**

❶ Find $(9x + 2) + (7x + 12)$.

Method 1 Add vertically.

$$
\begin{array}{r}
9x + 2 \\
(+) 7x + 12 \\
\hline
\boxed{16x + 14}
\end{array}
$$

Align $\boxed{\textbf{like}}$ terms.

Add.

Method 2 Add horizontally.

$(9x + 2) + (7x + 12)$

$\quad = (9x + 7x) + (2 + 12)$ Associative and Commutative Properties

$\quad = \boxed{\textbf{16x}} + \boxed{\textbf{14}}$

The sum is $\boxed{\textbf{16x + 14}}$.

❷ Find $(4x^2 + 11x - 3) + (-2x^2 + 5x - 7)$.

Method 1 Add vertically.

$$
\begin{array}{r}
4x^2 + 11x - 3 \\
(+) -2x^2 + 5x - 7 \\
\hline
\boxed{2x^2} + 16x \boxed{- 10}
\end{array}
$$

Method 2 Add horizontally.

$(4x^2 + 11x - 3) + (-2x^2 + 5x - 7)$

$\quad = (4x^2 - 2x^2) + \left(\boxed{\textbf{11x}} + \boxed{\textbf{5x}} \right) + (-3 - 7)$

$\quad = \boxed{\textbf{2x}^2} + 16x \boxed{- 10}$

The sum is $\boxed{\textbf{2x}^2 + \textbf{16x} - \textbf{10}}$.

3 Find $(15x^2 + 4) + (9x - 13)$.

$(15x^2 + 4) + (9x - 13) = 15x^2 +$ $\boxed{9x}$ $+ (4 - 13)$ Group like terms.

$= 15x^2 + 9x -$ $\boxed{9}$ Simplify.

The sum is $15x^2 + 9x -$ $\boxed{9}$.

---

4 Find $(3x^2 + 14x - 9) + (-6x + 1)$.

$$3x^2 + 14x - 9$$
$$(+) \qquad - 6x + 1$$

> Leave a space because there is no other term like $3x^2$.

$\boxed{3x^2}$ $+ 8x$ $\boxed{-8}$

The sum is $\boxed{3x^2 + 8x - 8}$.

Your Turn Add.

a. $(5x + 1) + (3x + 10)$

$8x + 11$

b. $(x^2 + 3x - 6) + (-3x^2 + 4x - 3)$

$-2x^2 + 7x - 9$

c. $(5x^2 + 2) + (2x - 9)$

$5x^2 + 2x - 7$

d. $(2x^2 + 4x - 7) + (-3x + 5)$

$2x^2 + x - 2$

EXAMPLE Use Polynomials to Solve a Problem

5 Find the measure of ∠A in the figure below.

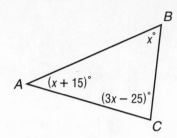

Write an equation to find the value of x.

The sum of the measures of the angles   equals   180

$(x + 15) + x + (3x - 25)$ $=$ 180   Write the equation.

$\left(\boxed{x + x + 3x}\right) + \left(\boxed{15 - 25}\right) = 180$ Group like terms.

$5x - 10 = 180$ Simplify.

$+\ \boxed{10}\ \ +\ \boxed{10}$ Add $\boxed{10}$ to each side.

$5x\qquad\quad = 190$ Simplify.

$\dfrac{5x}{5} = \dfrac{190}{5}$ Divide each side by 5.

$x = \boxed{38}$ Simplify.

Find the measure of ∠A.

$m\angle A = x + 15$ Write the expression for the measure of angle A.

$= \boxed{38} + 15$ Replace x with $\boxed{38}$.

$= \boxed{53}$ Simplify.

The measure of ∠A is $\boxed{53°}$.

HOMEWORK ASSIGNMENT

Page(s):

Exercises:

Your Turn Find the measure of ∠A in the figure below.

50° degrees

Subtracting Polynomials

WHAT YOU'LL LEARN

- Subtract polynomials.

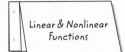

ORGANIZE IT

Record what you learn about subtracting polynomials in the Lesson 12-5 section of your Foldable journal.

Linear & Nonlinear Functions

EXAMPLES Subtract Polynomials

Subtract.

1 $(8c + 3) - (6c + 2)$

$$
\begin{array}{r}
8c + 3 \\
(-)\ 6c + 2 \\
\hline
2c + 1
\end{array}
$$

Align the terms.
Subtract.

The difference is $\boxed{2c + 1}$.

2 $(-2d^2 + 6d - 11) - (-3d + 4)$

$$
\begin{array}{r}
-2d^2 + 6d - 11 \\
(-)\qquad -3d + \ 4 \\
\hline
-2d^2 + 9d - 15
\end{array}
$$

Align the terms.
Subtract.

The difference is $\boxed{-2d^2 + 9d - 15}$.

EXAMPLES Subtract Using the Additive Inverse

3 Find $(6z + 1) - (2z - 5)$.

The additive inverse of $2z - 5$ is $\boxed{-2z + 5}$.

$(6z + 1) - (2z - 5)$

$\quad = (6z + 1) + (-2z + 5)$ To subtract $(2z - 5)$, add $(-2z + 5)$.

$\quad = (6z - 2z) + 1 + 5)$ Group like terms.

$\quad = 4z + 6$ Simplify by combining like terms.

The difference is $\boxed{4z + 6}$.

4 Find $(10f^2 - 15) - (-5f + 3)$.

The additive inverse of $-5f + 3$ is $\boxed{5f - 3}$.

$$
\begin{array}{r}
10f^2 \qquad -15 \\
(-)\qquad -5f + 3 \\
\hline
\end{array}
\longrightarrow
\begin{array}{r}
10f^2 \qquad -15 \\
(+)\qquad\ 5f - \ 3 \\
\hline
10f^2 + 5f - 18
\end{array}
$$

The difference is $\boxed{10f^2 + 5f - 18}$.

Your Turn Subtract.

a. $(6c + 5) - (2c + 2)$.

$$4c + 3$$

b. $(5d^2 + 2d + 10) - (-5d + 8)$.

$$5d^2 + 7d + 2$$

c. $(11z + 2) - (3z - 6)$.

$$8z + 8$$

d. $(12f^2 - 5) - (-2f + 4)$.

$$12f^2 + 2f - 9$$

EXAMPLE Use Polynomials to Solve a Problem

5 EXPERIMENTS Students are rolling identical marbles down two side-by-side ramps. The marble on ramp A rolls $3t^2 + 11t$ inches in t seconds. The marble on ramp B rolls $2t^2 + 4t$ inches in t seconds. How far apart are the marbles after 6 seconds?

Write an expression for the difference of the distances traveled by each marble.

Words — Marble A's distance minus marble B's distance.

Variable — $t = $ the time in seconds

Expression — $(3t^2 + 11t) - (2t^2 + 4t)$

$$
\begin{array}{r}
3t^2 + 11t \\
(-)\ 2t^2 + \ 4t \\
\hline
\end{array}
\quad \longrightarrow \quad
\begin{array}{r}
3t^2 + 11t \\
(+)\ 2t^2 - \ 4t \\
\hline
t^2 + \ 7t
\end{array}
$$

Now evaluate this expression for a time of 6 seconds.

$t^2 + 7t = (\boxed{6})^2 + 7(\boxed{6})$ Replace t with $\boxed{6}$.

$= \boxed{36} + 42$ or 78   Simplify.

After $\boxed{6}$ seconds, the cars are $\boxed{78}$ inches apart.

Your Turn Students are rolling identical marbles down two side-by-side ramps. The marble on ramp A rolls $4t^2 + 12t$ inches in t seconds. The marble on ramp B rolls $t^2 + 2t$ inches in t seconds. How far apart are the marbles after 5 seconds?

125 in.

HOMEWORK ASSIGNMENT

Page(s):

Exercises:

Multiplying and Dividing Monomials

WHAT YOU'LL LEARN

- Multiply and divide monomials.

KEY CONCEPT

Product of Powers To multiply powers with the same base, add their exponents.

FOLDABLES In the Lesson 12–6 section of your Foldable, record the product of powers rule.

EXAMPLE Multiply Powers

1 Find $7^6 \cdot 7^2$. Express using exponents.

$7^6 \cdot 7^2 = 7^{6 + 2}$ The common base is 7.

$= 7^8$ **Add** the exponents.

Check $7^6 \cdot 7^2 = (7 \cdot 7 \cdot 7 \cdot 7 \cdot 7 \cdot 7) \cdot (7 \cdot 7)$

$= 7 \cdot 7 \cdot 7 \cdot 7 \cdot 7 \cdot 7 \cdot 7 \cdot 7$

$= 7^8$

Your Turn Find $2^5 \cdot 2^4$. Express using exponents.

2^9

EXAMPLE Multiply Monomials

2 Find $7x^2(11x^4)$. Express using exponents.

$7x^2(11x^4) = (7 \cdot 11) \, (x^2 \cdot x^4)$ Comm. and Assoc. Properties.

$= (77) \, (x^{2 + 4})$ The common base is x.

$= 77x^6$ **Add** the exponents.

Your Turn Find $3x^2(-5x^5)$. Express using exponents.

$-15x^7$

EXAMPLE Divide Powers

Divide. Express using exponents.

KEY CONCEPT

Quotient of Powers To divide powers with the same base, subtract their exponents.

3 $\dfrac{6^{12}}{6^2}$

$\dfrac{6^{12}}{6^2} = 6^{12-2}$ The common base is $\boxed{6}$.

    $= \boxed{6^{10}}$ Simplify.

4 $\dfrac{a^{14}}{a^8}$

$\dfrac{a^{14}}{a^8} = a^{14-8}$ The common base is $\boxed{a}$.

    $= \boxed{a^6}$ Simplify.

Your Turn Divide. Express using exponents.

a. $\dfrac{3^{10}}{3^4}$

$\boxed{3^6}$

b. $\dfrac{x^{11}}{x^3}$

$\boxed{x^8}$

HOMEWORK ASSIGNMENT

Page(s): _____

Exercises: _____

_____

_____

Multiplying Monomials and Polynomials

WHAT YOU'LL LEARN

• Multiply monomials and polynomials.

FOLDABLES

ORGANIZE IT

In the Lesson 12-7 section of your Foldable, explain the Distributive Property. Be sure to include an example.

Linear & Nonlinear Functions

EXAMPLES Use the Distributive Property

1 Find $y(y + 12)$.

$y(y + 12) = y(\boxed{y}) + y(\boxed{12})$ Distributive Property

$= \boxed{y^2} + \boxed{12y}$ $y \cdot y = \boxed{y^2}$

The answer is $\boxed{y^2 + 12y}$.

2 Find $-6x(x + 3)$.

$-6x(x + 3) = -6x(\boxed{x}) + (-6x)(\boxed{3})$ Distributive Property

$= -6x^2 + (-18x)$ $-6 \cdot x \cdot x = -6x^2$

$= \boxed{-6x^2 - 18x}$ Definition of subtraction

The answer is $\boxed{-6x^2 - 18x}$.

Your Turn Multiply.

a. $y(y + 3)$

$\boxed{y^2 + 3y}$

b. $-2x(x + 6)$

$\boxed{-2x^2 - 12x}$

EXAMPLES Use the Product of Powers Rule

3 Find $7w(w^2 + 6)$.

$7w(w^2 + 6)$

$= \boxed{7w}(w^2) + \boxed{7w}(6)$ Distributive Property

$= \boxed{7w^3} + \boxed{42w}$ $7w(w^2) = 7w^{1 + 2}$ or $\boxed{7w^3}$

The answer is $\boxed{7w^3 + 42w}$.

④ Find $9t(t^2 + 6t - 4)$.

$9t(t^2 + 6t - 4)$

    $= 9t[t^2 + 6t + (-4)]$ Rewrite $t^2 + 6t - 4$ as $t^2 + 6t + (-4)$.

    $= 9t(t^2) +$ **$9t(6t)$** $+ 9t(-4)$ Distributive Property

    $=$ **$9t^3$** $+$ **$54t^2$** $+$ **$(-36t)$**   Simplify.

    $=$ **$9t^3 + 54t^2 - 36t$**   Definition of subtraction

The answer is **$9t^3 + 54t^2 - 36t$** .

Your Turn **Multiply.**

a. $3w(w^2 - 8)$

$3w^3 - 24w$

b. $5t(t^2 + 7t - 6)$

$5t^3 + 35t^2 - 30t$

HOMEWORK ASSIGNMENT

Page(s):

Exercises:

BRINGING IT ALL TOGETHER

STUDY GUIDE

FOLDABLES™	**VOCABULARY PUZZLEMAKER**	**BUILD YOUR VOCABULARY**
Use your **Chapter 12 Foldable** to help you study for your chapter test.	To make a crossword puzzle, word search, or jumble puzzle of the vocabulary words in Chapter 12, go to: www.glencoe.com/sec/math/t_resources/free/index.php	You can use your completed **Vocabulary Builder** *(page 308)* to help you solve the puzzle.

12-1
Linear and Nonlinear Functions

Write *linear* or *nonlinear* to name the kind of function described.

1. constant rate change

> **linear**

2. graph that is a curve

> **nonlinear**

3. power of *x* may be greater than one

> **nonlinear**

4. equation has the form $-y = mx + b$

> **linear**

5. Name the kind of function represented. Explain your reasoning.

x	−3	0	3	6
y	10	1	10	37

> **Nonlinear; rate of change is not constant.**

12-2
Graphing Quadratic Functions

Determine whether each equation represents a quadratic function. Write *yes* or *no*.

6. $y = 3x - 5$

> **no**

7. $y = 6 - x^2$

> **yes**

8.

> **yes**

9. Explain how to graph a quadratic function.

> **Make a table of values, plot the points, and connect the points with a smooth curve.**

12-3
Simplifying Polynomials

Write *true* or *false* beside each statement. If the statement is false, write the correct word in place of the underlined word.

10. The product of $4y$ and $-6y$ is a <u>polynomial</u>.　| **false; monomial** |

11. The expression $x + 5$ is a <u>polynomial</u> with two terms.　| **true** |

12. To simplify a polynomial, combine <u>exponents</u>.　| **false; like terms** |

Simplify each polynomial. If the polynomial cannot be simplified, write *simplest form*.

13. $2x^2 + 3x - x^2 + 4$　　**14.** $6c - 4d - 1$　　**15.** $8 + 3a - 10 - a + 2b$

| $x^2 + 3x + 4$ | | **simplest form** | | $2a + 2b - 2$ |

12-4
Adding Polynomials

Determine whether each vertical addition can be performed as written. Explain.

16.　　$x^2 + 5x - 6$
　　　$(+)\ 2x^2 + 3x + 4$

| **Yes; like terms are aligned.** |

17.　　$x^2 + 6$
　　　$(+)\ 2x^2 - x$

| **No; 6 and $-x$ are not like terms.** |

Rewrite each sum of polynomials vertically. Then add.

18. $(3d^2 + 14d - 2) + (-d^2 + 3d + 5)$　　**19.** $(2n^2 + 3) + (n^2 - 5n + 1)$

| $3d^2 + 14d - 2$ |
| $(+)\ \ -d^2 + 3d + 5$ |
| $2d^2 + 17d + 3$ |

| $2n^2 \ + 3$ |
| $(+)\ \ n^2 - 5n + 1$ |
| $3n^2 - 5n + 4$ |

12-5
Subtracting Polynomials

Rewrite each difference of polynomials as a sum of polynomials. Then add.

20. $(7x + 5) - (4x - 3)$

| $(7x + 5) + (-4x + 3);$ $3x + 8$ |

21. $(-3c^2 + 2c - 1) - (-c^2 - c - 2)$

| $(-3c^2 + 2c - 1) + (c^2 + c + 2);\ -2c^2 + 3c + 1$ |

22. $(m^2 + 3m - 6) - (m^2 + 1)$

$(m^2 + 3m - 6) +$
$(-m^2 - 1); 3m - 7$

23. $(-6s + 9) - (4s^2 + 2s - 3)$

$(-6s + 9) + (-4s^2 - 2s$
$+ 3); -4s^2 - 8s + 12$

12-6

Multiplying and Dividing Monomials

Complete each sentence.

24. To multiply powers with the same base, ⟦ **add** ⟧ their exponents.

25. To divide powers with the same base, ⟦ **subtract** ⟧ their exponents.

26. Can $a^4 \cdot b^3$ be multiplied by adding exponents? Explain.

No, because they don't have the same base.

27. Can $\dfrac{8^3}{4^3}$ be divided by subtracting exponents? Explain.

No, because they don't have the same base.

Multiply or divide. Express using exponents.

28. $5^2 \cdot 5^6$

5^8

29. $(8x^3)(-3x^9)$

$-24x^{12}$

30. $\dfrac{2^5}{2^2}$

2^3

31. $\dfrac{18a^7}{6a^3}$

$3a^4$

12–7

Multiplying Monomials and Polynomials

32. Explain what is done at each step in the following problem.
$3x(x^2 + 5x - 2)$

$= 3x[x^2 + 5x + (-2)]$ **Rewrite $x^2 + 5x - 2$ as $x^2 + 5x + (-2)$.**

$= 3x(x^2) + 3x(5x) + 3x(-2)$ **Distributive Property**

$= 3x^3 + 15x^2 + (-6x)$ **Simplify.**

$= 3x^3 + 15x^2 - 6x$ **Definition of subtraction**

ARE YOU READY FOR THE CHAPTER TEST?

Math Online

Visit **msmath3.net** to access your textbook, more examples, self-check quizzes, and practice tests to help you study the concepts in Chapter 12.

Check the one that applies. Suggestions to help you study are given with each item.

☐ **I completed the review of all or most lessons without using my notes or asking for help.**

- You are probably ready for the Chapter Test.

- You may want to take the Chapter 12 Practice Test on page 595 of your textbook as a final check.

☐ **I used my Foldable or Study Notebook to complete the review of all or most lessons.**

- You should complete the Chapter 12 Study Guide and Review on pages 593–594 of your textbook.

- If you are unsure of any concepts or skills, refer to the specific lesson(s).

- You may also want to take the Chapter 12 Practice Test on page 595.

☐ **I asked for help from someone else to complete the review of all or most lessons.**

- You should review the examples and concepts in your Study Notebook and Chapter 12 Foldable.

- Then complete the Chapter 12 Study Guide and Review on pages 593–594 of your textbook.

- If you are unsure of any concepts or skills, refer to the specific lesson(s).

- You may also want to take the Chapter 12 Practice Test on page 595.

Student Signature

Parent/Guardian Signature

Teacher Signature